Published by

Turrill Ltd.

Copyright Turrill Ltd.
First published in 1986 by the Institute of Health Service Managers.
Second Edtion 1993.

ISBN 0 9521207 1 2

Typeset by:
Turrill Ltd.,
The Old Vicarage,
Great Thirkleby,
Thirsk,
North Yorkshire YO7 2AT.

Printed by:
G.H.Smith and Son,
Easingwold,
North Yorkshire.

Change and Innovation

A Challenge for the NHS

Tony Turrill

FOREWORDS
to the first edition

From Sir John Harvey-Jones, then chairman ICI PLC

It gives me great pleasure to write a few introductory words to Tony Turrill's excellent monograph on Change and Innovation.

Suffice it to say that both of us came out of the same stable and have learnt our lessons about change from identical sources. I was interested when reading the monograph to see that all the references were ones that I knew and indeed, in many cases, referred to people I had worked with.

It is perhaps impertinent for someone from one industry to offer advice to another on change and its necessity. However, from the point of view of a friendly, supportive, interested and concerned layman, the National Health Service requires every assistance that it can get from us all. It must by now be clear to everyone that there will never be enough money to provide the sort of health care that we would like to see in a caring society. We therefore have to learn by experimentation and adaptation to achieve more with less, and to improve our ways of doing things. It is only by a further release of the energy of the many dedicated people in the NHS that this can be achieved. Nobody doubts that everyone in that service gives of their best and we cannot do more unless we change our approaches and our methods. This, as I see it, is the challenge and the task and this is what Tony Turrill's monograph aims to assist.

For everyone's sake, whether users, supporters, or practitioners in your service, I hope very much that the book achieves its objective.

From Len Peach, then NHS Chief Executive Officer, NHS Management Board.

The National Health Service is undergoing the pressures of change at an unprecedented rate and in probably unprecedented volume. The growth in demand for patient services enhanced by demographic factors and medical technology; the impact on resources of financial allocation according to the RAWP formula; the reorganisation and redistribution of manpower and skills produced by moves towards care in the community; and all the managerial revolution produced by the Griffiths' Report are making the tasks of leadership and management more difficult in application though more rewarding in success. Imperfectly understood and sometimes opposed or not accepted because of the confusion produced by their interaction, these trends and policies create major challenges for management seeking to make the most effective use of available resources in the implementation of new policies, practices and styles.

Knowledge of change, innovation theory and process is therefore of prime importance to all wishing to manage effectively in the current environment.

These are important lessons too for other organisations and institutions. In the United Kingdom there is a need to create a climate of innovation and change as a way of life. 'Not invented here' still seems to form a substantial part of the British tradition whereas our competitors, notably those in the Far East, continue to demonstrate a willingness to scour the world for good ideas, to import them, improve them and then to re-export the quality products which the customer demands. A number of British companies have undergone substantial reorganisation produced by the economic circumstances of the past few years, with management aided in this task by crises which produce new attitudes towards change - at least temporarily. The threats of bankruptcy, unemployment and in other cases the availability of share ownership or financial rewards has aided this process though it has yet to be seen how far management has been successful in inculcating in these organisations a genuine spirit of innovation and change as a way of life.

It is the search for this spirit within the NHS which has inspired the publication of this book. The pressures which have produced the process of change in industry do not exist to the same extent within the service and so the task of management is more difficult. Bankruptcy and financial rewards are not the main spring of action. Management unaided by external pressures must make its own change process, and must build a climate at Region, District or Unit level which enables the individual and the group to understand and to take part in the events which are shaping their working lives and which will contribute to improvements in patient care. There are many valuable lessons and hints in the pages of this monograph, drawn from Tony Turrill's own experiences and the writing of the acknowledged masters of this subject in the world of management teaching. I hope that you find this book as entertaining as I did and also as informative and helpful in managing the surge of innovation and change which we are experiencing and will experience during the next few years.

CONTENTS

Preface to the second edition

When the time arrived to prepare a second edition of this monograph, my first assumption was that so much had happened since 1986 that it would need to be considerably revamped, if not totally rewritten. However, on re-reading the original, I was drawn to the conclusion that the basic principles it describes, the questions it raises and the tools it provides are as relevant today as they were when the first edition was written. Nevertheless, the experience of seven more years working as a change consultant and a plethora of dissertations from the management gurus tempted me towards an extensive revision until I remembered the old adage: *"If it aint broken don't fix it"*. Despite Tom Peters' maxim, *"If you think it aint broken, you haven't looked hard enough"*, I have chosen to stick largely to the proven text. The opportunity has been taken to delete some minor details which were anachronistic and to correct some editorial errors - parts of the first edition perhaps being too close for comfort to Grauniadese.

In addition, at the end of each chapter, a paragraph has been added - "Approaching the New Millennium (1993 edition)". This device enables me to draw attention to any significant events which currently face us.

Tony Turrill, (May 1993).

Acknowledgements

I am conscious that the name Richard Beckhard does not feature in the references at the end of each chapter. This is because so many of the ideas have their origins in his work and writings that it would not have been practical to refer to each individually. His books on strategies of Organisation Development and, with Reuben Harris, on Organisational Transition (Addison-Wesley), are the foundation for much of what follows. If there appears at times to be plagiarism, my excuse is that it would be impossible to write anything about change without trespassing on the territory that he made his own.

Alex Graham's name must also be written large. I have had the pleasure of working with him on many workshops that we have run for NHS teams and seeing him in action as a consultant. Again it would be impossible for me to distinguish which of the ideas, in what follows, are his babies. It is safer to assume that his wise counsel and unstinted efforts played a major part in the whole process. My colleague David Wilson's support must also be mentioned. Again we have worked together on many workshops and debated many of these ideas. Both he and Alex have made a number of helpful comments on drafts, for which I am very grateful.

The origins of some of the techniques listed in the appendices are lost in the mists of time, I know that many were developed and refined by groups of managers in various parts of the country. I feel confident that they would be delighted to know that their ideas are still being used and hope that readers will continue to develop them further.

If I had realised how much effort was involved in writing a monograph, I doubt whether I would have started. I said in the first edition that my wife, therefore, deserves special mention, not only for reading and commenting on the proofs but also for accepting yet another delay in completing our bathroom and that "perhaps, if this book sells enough copies, we shall be able to get a man in and she will forgive me". I finished the bathroom - we now need a man to re-decorate the rooms beneath it.

PART 1
SOME KEY CHANGE ISSUES

This section of the monograph discusses some of the main issues surrounding organisational change and innovation. It may well raise as many questions as it provides answers. This is deliberate and reflects a firm belief that, when introducing change, the journey is at least as important as the destination. Each organisation must find its own answers with its own people. There is no short cut, no substitute, for involving people in order to generate their commitment. It is this commitment which will embed the change in the organisation and ensure its survival.

Part 2 describes some tools which can help generate some of the detailed answers.

Chapter 1 | INTRODUCTION

Lord give me strength to change the things that can be changed, the tolerance to accept those that cannot and the wisdom to know the difference between them.

A morning prayer

If you can keep your head when all about you are losing theirs, then ... you just don't understand the nature of the mess we're in.

almost Kipling

Why a monograph on change and innovation when so much has been written already? What has this additional and relatively small volume got to offer? It's perhaps easier to start by saying what it isn't, rather than what it is. It certainly isn't a report of a new, objective piece of academic research. Neither is it a definitive statement of how to manage change and be innovative. After many years working in changing organisations, the only thing I am sure of is that there is no such thing as one right way, although, some ways are more right that others. The world is a complex and irrational place. Change is a messy, iterative process. Just when you think you have arrived, you find you have hardly begun. What works for me, doesn't work for you. What is perfectly acceptable in District X, is instantly rejected in District Y. Even more irritatingly, what worked so well last time fails miserably the next - even in the same place, with the same people. I find the following quotation comforting and hope that it is true.

> "When you go through an inordinately messy, sloppy, fouled up, mucked up, seven year process [.. of change], you say to yourself 'any idiot could have done it better than that! Let's get organised the next time round' and in that single phrase 'Let's get organised ....' lie the seeds of subsequent disaster .... in a messy world the only way to proceed is by constant experimentation: don't just stand there, do something".[1]

If it's that unpredictable why bother writing about it, or, even more unwisely, attempt to make a living by working with people who are trying to "do something", in all this chaos? I guess, for most of us who do, it's a mixture of having no choice but to live in the world as it is and, perversely, finding working with the uncertainty a very exciting and stimulating process. I once knew an engineer who was prone to accuse "those up there" of always changing the goal posts. When he left the organisation, he was presented with a pair of lovingly crafted, miniature rugby posts. They could be adjusted to any width, the cross-bar placed at any height and the posts placed anywhere on the pitch. Most of us who work for the NHS would recognise that this is the game we have to learn to play. This booklet aims to present a few, relatively simple principles, which help some people play the game and which they hang onto when all else fails. It may identify some of the hazards and traps so that, if you fall into them, they at least look familiar. It will suggest some basic tools for thinking about how to have another go at getting out of them. In a very subjective way, it will also point to some of the literature that I have enjoyed reading and found helpful.

Reference:

1. T. Peters and N. Austin, *A Passion for Excellence*, (William Collins 1985)

Chapter 2 | THE CONTINUING DRIVE FOR CHANGE AND INNOVATION

Change is not made without inconvenience even from worse to better.

Richard Hooker, Johnson's English Dictionary, 1600

Not so much a programme, more a way of life.

BBC TV 1960s

We have in the past tended to think of change in packages - discrete projects or programmes associated with the start up of this hospital, the closure of that institution, the introduction of a new structure, the adaptation to a new minister or a different set of government policies. There is now so much change, which many perceive as being imposed by "them" on us, that change has for most of us become a way of life. "Why start another round of reorganisation before we have finished the last one?" is a familiar cri de coeur. It would perhaps be comforting for some to think that this was a temporary phase. "Given a little time and a change of government, it will all go away and we can get back to looking after the patients, doing research, practising surgery or whatever." In uncertain times anything is possible. Perhaps keeping one's head down and waiting for it all to sort itself out is a good strategy for survival. Who knows for certain? At least a lowered head is out of the line of fire. On the other hand, it may turn out that burying one's head in the sand leads to a life in the desert. We all know people, successful ones too, whose careers have evaporated overnight and who have been faced, sometimes more than once, with picking up the pieces and starting again. Not only individuals but organisations have crashed, many were household names that seemed part of the fabric of everyday life. Some innovative, well managed organisations, that fought to adapt to the turbulent world, have survived. The less sensitive and proactive have died or seem terminally ill, as they engage in spasms of takeovers and mergers. Whatever it is that is causing the turbulence is affecting all parts of society. We might be forgiven if we argued that the NHS is a special case and should be sheltered from the worst of the storms. Most who remember the days before "socialised medicine" will feel protective about the NHS. We are, however, living in the same turbulent environment as our wealth generating colleagues. Many of the factors affecting them equally affect us and, if we are to survive, we need to be aware of this and act accordingly.

The UK is no longer a fat economy. We no longer have a surfeit of cash. As a nation we have to make choices and set priorities. As we lose our oil cushion, and assuming no major change in the way we run our national business, the choices may well become harsher. Science and technology continue to present an ever increasing array of high-tech. solutions at an every increasing rate. Anyone trying to buy the best computer knows the problem only too well. It often seems to take longer to select the best option and sanction the expenditure than to develop a better machine. This better machine then needs to be included in the options, the original decision is revised and sanction again sought, by which time a third generation machine is available and so on, ad infinitum.

In the 50s and 60s, on the people side, life was orderly. Good organisations were paternalistic and authority was largely respected. T J Watson, the Chief Executive of IBM, talking of his highly successful company, could say, "we believed that if we respected our people and helped them respect themselves, the company would make the most profit". (Notice the possessive pronoun). The obverse of this coin, stated by an IBM manager, was "after working here for a while you don't even know how to make your own hotel reservation".[1] Many large organisations, formally and informally, reflected the recent military experience of their employees. The work-force often split into officers (the senior managers), warrant officers, (first-line supervisors) and other ranks (the labour force). Most employees could look forward to continuous employment from their twenties to their sixties. For the "officers", good or even adequate performance led to an orderly career progression. A few warrant officers were allowed to cross the barriers and be promoted into the ranks of managers. Other ranks, the payroll, were of course a different breed. They needed clear instructions, detailed supervision and had to be controlled by a mixture of carrots (bonus schemes) and sticks (disciplinary procedures). Men worked and women knew their place in the world - at home raising the family. Life isn't like that any more. People demand a say in their working destiny, we are seeing a healthy disrespect of "the right to manage", barriers are coming down, alternatives to hierarchies emerging. Common pay structures and harmony of conditions for all employees are becoming commonplace. To have several careers in a life-time is no longer unusual. Even in the NHS, despite its enormous female fall-out from National Trainees, we are seeing increasing numbers of women at work, outside the traditional areas of nursing, "para-medicine" and hotel services and not only in lower levels of management.

Many would argue that we are sitting on top of a societal paradigm shift, as significant to us in organisational terms as the San Andreas fault is seismologically to San Francisco and as likely to erupt with explosive violence, if ignored. Its components have often been described, perhaps most clearly, if in American terms, by Naisbitt[2] as follows:

From	To
Industrial Society	Information Society
Forced Technology	High Tech/High touch*
National Economy	World Economy
Short Term	Long Term
Centralisation	Decentralisation
Institutional Help	Self Help
Representative Democracy	Participative Democracy
Hierarchies	Networking
North	South**
Either/Or	Multiple Options

* High touch, the increasing need for technology
to be user friendly if it is to be acceptable.

** The American shift from North to South coincidentally
describes the continuing morbidity of the industrial North in the UK.

If this paradigm shift is truly happening and properly described above, it follows that we must be prepared to continue to handle a period of turbulence and change for some considerable time to come. It is also commonsense that any new systems we establish or changes that we make to our old ways should be congruent with the new paradigm not the old. The older ones amongst us may sometimes think we have seen it all before and can therefore apply well-proven solutions. We should be forgiven but not listened to for what is probably a loss of clear vision with approaching senility. There may well also be an element of wish fulfilment, hoping that, if history would only repeat itself, we might understand it better the second time around - rather like the repeat of a difficult Le Carre TV whodunit. The current preoccupation with the way industry does/did things and about attempts to translate their solutions to the NHS in the 1990s, may prove to be an example of this in action, if we worry insufficiently about the changing context.

Of course, there is a risk that the uncertainty will in itself induce organisational paralysis. If everything is unpredictable, why prepare for the future? Because, it is possible to use the overall driving forces to make best guesses about how they will affect the issue being considered[3]. As an illustration, the issue of staffing in the NHS is so significant that we need to get it right, both in terms of quality and quantity. It seems unlikely that the excellent performance appraisal, career planning and development systems that the best American or British companies used in the past, will, without change and adaptation, meet our or their needs for a very different future. For example, organisational grooming of a number of crown princes is only relevant when there is some certainty about the shape, or even the existence, of a kingdom. The very uncertainty of the future leads to the conclusion that flexible processes for changing individual careers will be at least as important as concrete organisational succession plans. We will need systems which allow individuals to join and leave the organisation at several points in their career. With a continuing move away from hierarchies and a need for greater efficiency, the number of "top" jobs will shrink and promotion will be less available as a reward. We will have a surfeit of people with potential to "get to the top". Concerns will probably move away from identifying potential senior managers and from boss-subordinate relationships, towards procedures which encourage staff to work in flexible groups of equals, which have no long term permanence and where reward is more closely allied to achievement. The dilution of the organisation's hierarchical power, in combination with the move from institutional to self-help, should lead us to explore ways in which individuals control their own destiny, handle multiple career options and follow paths which match both their needs and those of the organisation. Some authors[4] have argued that we shall see a move away from single employment, perhaps working part time for one organisation, part-time in some small business and part-time, unpaid, for some activity we value. The changes in family life, the liberation of women, shared responsibility for bringing up children and growing numbers of one parent families, will force us to accept new patterns of employment. As hierarchical, career-ladder climbing becomes less important, it will be easier for one parent to take time out from paid employment and for us to find ways of enabling their later return. David Clutterbuck[5] argued that we are already seeing major shifts in how, where, why and when we work. He commented that in the UK, between 1984 and 1985, of the 263,000 new jobs created, 213,000 were part-time for women and this trend continues. It is relatively easy to move from such speculations to a recognition that we need to rethink our whole approach to career planning, as traditionally practised in large organisations. It is a harder, but not impossible task, to suggest components of a more appropriate future system, based on some of the ideas explored briefly above.

References :

1. F. Levering et al, *The Hundred Best Companies to work for in America,* Addison-Wesley, 1984.

2. John Naisbitt, *Megatrends,* ,Warner, New York, 1982.

3. W. Bennis and B. Nanus, *Leaders,*, Harper and Row, 1985. p 167 et seq.

4. Derek Sheen, *Change,* MCB Publications.

5. David Clutterbuck et al, *New Patterns of Work,* Gower Press 1985.

Approaching the New Millennium (1993 edition).

A favourite metaphor for organisational life in the 80s was the white water river. The big ships that had prospered in the calmer waters of the previous decades were visibly struggling in the more tempestuous waters generated by an increasingly turbulent environment. If organisations were to stand any chance of surviving, they had to find new vessels which could respond more rapidly and flexibly to the unpredictable hazards of the violent torrents. Increasingly, small seemed beautiful and although rafts were inherently less comfortable, they were more likely to survive than the luxury liners of old. Small, highly competent, outward looking, enthusiastic crews operating with dedication to a common aim began to replace cumbersome hierarchies and rigid bureaucracies. At the end of the decade, even the apparently impregnable and highly centralised IBM was forced to consider new ways - perhaps too late in view of its recent multi-billion dollar losses and waves of redundancy.

The early nineties have not brought any respite. The existing driving forces remain and new ones have appeared. Technology moves on apace - in the NHS, for example, key-hole surgery has become commonplace and who knows what great strides in genetics the multinational project to map the human genes will bring. The attempt to combat AIDS is forcing once competing companies to build strategic alliances. Europe is in turmoil as it redraws its political boundaries and in deep recession - its capacity for wealth generation threatened as manufacturing moves away to the Pacific Rim. Deregulation and privatisation continue as countries seek to square the impossible circle of matching resources to an ever increasing demand. If the turbulence reached gale force in the 80s, the hurricane warnings have now been hoisted. In response, our largest manufacturer, ICI, has demerged, splitting into two separate companies, each in turn dividing into a number of highly independent small businesses. The NHS has separated into purchasers and providers - many provider units have in turn broken their activities down into separate "directorates" that are managed much closer to the patients and can respond more rapidly to changing demands.

A different metaphor likens today's management tasks to climbing the north face of Everest. In the 80s, some of us made it to Base Camp, no mean feat at that altitude. We now face the mountain proper and there is probably not enough oxygen to go round.

Summary

The forces driving organisational change are likely to be with us for the foreseeable future. They are not peculiar to the NHS. Whilst we can learn from the ways others are handling the new paradigm, we should approach older "well tried" models with caution. We are most likely to be successful if our activities are congruent with our best guesses of the future than if based on the admittedly more certain past.

Chapter 3 | THE DILEMMAS OF THE CHANGE PROCESS

There is nothing more difficult, more perilous to conduct, or more uncertain in its success, than to take the lead in a new order of things, because the innovator has for enemies all those who have done well under the old conditions, and lukewarm defenders in those who may do well under the new. This coolness arises partly from fear of the opponents who have the law on their side and partly from the fear of men, who do not readily believe in new things until they have experience of them.

Machiavelli

Let's find out what everyone is doing and then stop everyone from doing it.

A.P. Herbert

The basic elements that make up a successful change process are so simple, straightforward and well documented that I can't help feeling that, despite Machiavelli's well known words of caution, it ought to be easier to be innovative. The problems seem to lie around balancing a number of key dilemmas, without compromising the principles involved.

The key dilemmas include:

- A need for experimentation *vs* a need to be right
- Powerful leadership *vs* empowered followers
- Managing the present *vs* managing the change
- Handling the environment *vs* building the internal organisation
- Sustaining simple beliefs vs handling complex issues.

The first step for any change manager (or should it be leader?) might well be to examine where he sits on the horns of these dilemmas; accepting that, whatever he does, he is likely to end up feeling sore. Some of these issues will be the subject of a more detailed examination later but let's consider some of the problems first; sharpen the horns, without, as yet, thinking about solutions.

This dilemma is probably closely connected with one of our national characteristics. Whenever we think about change, we want to be certain that it will work out all right before we start. We don't suffer fools gladly and nobody wants to be mistaken for one by not having foreseen what, with hindsight, is the obvious. As a nation, "Catch 'em doing something wrong" seems to be our motto rather than Blanchard's famous phrase "Catch 'em doing something right"[1].

That widely respected Irish philosopher, Murphy, makes a highly relevant point in the most famous of his laws. "Murphy's law of the Universe", stated simply, says that:

> "If it can go wrong it will."

The first corollary of Murphy's Universal Law is also worth noting:

> "It is the factor that you positively decide to ignore that always proves to be the most important."

Most managers would philosophically acknowledge the truth of the law but are nevertheless willing to allocate hundreds of man hours to cerebral activity, in the hope that they will develop the perfect change plan and be the first man or women to get it completely right, first time. There are so many factors which might be significant, so many options that need to be considered, that what began as a basically simple process now looks extremely complicated, even dangerous. Change, instead of being fun, is viewed as something that should carry a government health warning; "involvement in change can have a disastrous effect on your career".

The American consultant, Tom Peters[2], in his comments about the Myths of Innovation takes longer than Murphy to say much the same thing:

> "[it is a myth that] substantial strategic/technological planning greatly increases the odds of a no surprises outcome. Though you must be thoughtful in order to be roughly in the right arena, innovation ... is highly unpredictable and the context and configuration must be predicated on uncertainty and ambiguity"

An Experimental Approach vs Getting it Right

Whilst it would be wrong to argue for no thought and no planning, it is also worth remembering that Murphy is perhaps best remembered for the incident which led to his first great law of change inertia. When asked by a passing English visitor how to get to Dublin, he replied "If I were you, Sohrr, I wouldn't start from here". Later research enabled him to state the law numerically thus:

"The number of reasons for not starting any change programme is always greater than 101."

Typical examples would include, as well as being in the wrong place,

- It isn't the right time.
- We don't have the right resources.
- The circumstances will be better next week, month, year.
- It is too soon after the last one.
- We need more data.
- We really need to convene a multi-disciplinary working party to look into it.
- We don't want change for change's sake.
- We need evolution not revolution.
- We must wait until ...everyone is in post, the structures have been agreed, the government changes, the committee reports etc., & etc.

John Harvey-Jones, then chairman of ICI, captured the issue and his own rather different philosophy, when he said that his problem was not to get the ship (ICI) moving in the right direction but to get it moving at all: once it was under way, it could be made to jib and tack appropriately, in order to get on the right course.

Peters' (loc. cit) similar experimental philosophy is encapsulatedin chapter 4, where visionary leadership sets an entrepreneurial climate which legitimises experimentation, a climate where success is rewarded and people learn from their mistakes.

Powerful Leaders vs Empowered Followers

The role of the leader in change is well documented,[2,3,4] and it is clear that without major and sustained commitment from the top of the organisation, change initiatives eventually flounder. Rosabeth Kanter describes[5] a number of isolated innovators, "working against the grain", who managed to bring about some significant changes without the commitment of their top management. However, without exception, their interventions could not be sustained. It wasn't until Harvey-Jones was in a position in ICI which enabled him to pull all the levers[4] that the giant really awakened. Up to that time, even in his own neck of the woods, change had been sporadic. People therefore fall into the trap of thinking of change as being "top driven", imposed from above. Those who worry about the nuances of language will prefer "top led". When we talk of organisational change in the NHS, we need to keep reminding ourselves that the only worthwhile change is an improvement in the service to the individual patient, or society at large. Change is measured in the things that people do differently and hopefully better, especially those in direct contact with the patient. Those at the grass roots have the direct knowledge of what needs altering. With their commitment anything is possible, without it, nothing is. The dilemma lies in how to achieve the necessary overall top direction whilst encouraging change at the operational level. How is the energy of the majority to be released whilst ensuring it is effectively channelled rather then constrained? How do you get the power down to where it can be used?

Managing the Present vs Managing the Change

An effective organisation has a number of repertoires which it uses to "deliver the goods", whatever the goods are. The range of associated systems for running today's organisations require managing and can not be ignored. The process of change and transition is also an activity in its own right, different from managing the present: again the associated systems require managerial time and effort. The difference is that these change systems can be ignored. Ignoring the present might lead to a simple incident escalating fairly quickly into patient complaints, the attention of the press, government enquiries, questions in the House and so on. Ignoring managing the change just means that the future will be a little late arriving this year. Unless proper provision is made to allocate resources to change management, the present always wins and hence the future never arrives. Things don't get better, often they get worse, the present then demands more attention and the organisation spirals downwards. The first part of this dilemma is straightforward. How do you allocate resources to both the present demands and to the change process, assuming you have enough to go round?

The second part of this dilemma is more intangible. Organisations that routinely deliver the "right goods", at the right time, at the right quality, to the right place, often develop bureaucratic tendencies and attract bureaucrats to work in them. Bureaucracies have an inherent difficulty in coping with change, the derivation of the very word implies that. Bureaucracies are based on the premise that the organisation is largely static so that the best procedures can be developed, instructions written and placed in the "bureau", later to be used, in a precise way, by the prescribed job holder. All of this requires a degree of certainty, of predictability. Yet, uncertainty and ambiguity are the essence of change. The processes required to manage transition are therefore different and need different sorts of managers. More fundamentally still, maybe the steady state needs managers and the change process needs a leader[3]. How do you sustain a bureaucracy and an innovative organisation at one and the same time? How do you handle the inevitable conflicts between the bureaucrat and the entrepreneur?

Looking Outwards vs Looking Inwards

All organisations exist in an environment which is itself changing, continually making new demands on the organisation and expecting new responses from it. The world is littered with the debris of organisations who got their act together, set about changing the way their organisation worked but failed to keep a weather eye on the outside world sufficiently to be able to trim their sails to changes in the wind. If the balance of this dilemma tips too far the other way, there is a real danger that the environment is very well understood and regulated but the organisation has no energy left to meet its demands. To pursue the nautical metaphor, an alternative risk is that the organisation changes tack with every slight variation in the direction of the wind and ends up travelling in circles.

Simple Beliefs vs Complex Issues

The number of issues that will arise in any change programme are legion and very few can be ignored. There is a real danger that the trees will obscure the wood. What have long winded union negotiations, CHC meetings, redundant friends, interviews with the press, feelings of inadequacy, the MEC, the latest DHSS circular and a battle over funding with Region and the District next door to do with a determination to improve the lot of the mentally handicapped? The dilemma for the change leader (or is it manager?) is how to keep the principles in view whilst dealing with the detail. If you bought the idea that an organisation rests on a deep belief in the value of people and respect for their individuality, how do you square that with making twenty of them redundant?

At the beginning of this chapter, reference was made to the basic simplicity of the processes of change. Before describing them in more detail, in the next chapter, what are the basic elements of the change process? The first is an agreed understanding of the purpose of the enterprise. What is it there for, what is its mission in life? Some people call this the organisation's core purpose. Secondly, there needs to be a vision of the desired future, a clear picture of what the organisation is aiming at, which the whole organisation shares and which will pull the organisation forward. This desirable future must then be compared with the present condition in order to define, in some detail, the size and shape of the work of the transition. All that then remains is to find the appropriate resources, to establish an organisational climate (chapter 5) in which people learn from their incvitable mistakes, making plenty of them but never the same ones twice and finally to provide the necessary leadership (chapter 6) to help people persist.

References :

1. K. Blanchard and S. Johnson, *The One Minute Manager*, Collins, Willows 1983.

2. T.J. Peters and N. Austin, *A Passion For Excellence*, Collins 1985.

3. W. Bennis and B. Nanus, *Leaders*, Harper and Row, 1985.

4. Andrew Pettigrew, *The Awakening Giant*.

5. Rosabeth Kanter, *The Change Masters*, Counterpoint 1983.

Approaching the New Millennium (1993 Edition).

The dilemmas facing change managers/leaders have not decreased. Today, as never before, management is about handling conflicting alternatives, achieving conflicting goals - managing paradox. Some additional examples of today's dilemmas would include:-

Tight objectives - Moving Targets. Precise goals need to be set but constantly altered to match the changing situation. Management is now less about rigid planning more about being ready to seize opportunities.

Individual accountability - Team Working. People are being held individually accountable and so rewarded for their achievements but often against objectives which can only be achieved by the combined effort of multi-disciplinary groups.

Conflict - Consensus. Organisations require processes for fostering argument and agreement, divergence and convergence - for resolving conflicts often rooted in different, deeply held values.

Career Security - Flexible Staffing. Organisations are continually reshaping and renewing themselves. This has led to massive uncertainty in manpower forecasting, career planning and job security. Yet, individuals need personal security, if they are to take the risks that the changing situation demands.

High Quality - Low Cost. Increasing concerns for quality will need to be married with lower costs - learning to do more for less but better.

Compete - Collaborate. The fight for survival is forging new partnerships between public and private sectors, between customers and suppliers, between management and the work-force and, above all between different professions. The partners are nevertheless competing for a share of increasingly tight resources.

Open Information - Minimal Reporting. If the necessary, active response to change is widely spread around all levels of the organisation, information will need to be open, readily available to all but in ways which avoid swamping individuals. It is time to stop measuring everything. Systems must be developed to measure only the really vital elements of performance. Information will need to be collected and presented in ways which meet the needs of operational staff rather than being imposed from the top.

Robust Values -New Perspectives. The core employees must cherish the history and nurture the values of the organisation but must also work with a shifting network of individuals and organisations, accepting the new perspectives they bring.

In this overall scenario, the key dilemma is undoubtedly being simultaneously **"Loose and Tight"**. Tolerating, even encouraging, variety in local solutions whilst being fanatically committed to the central ideals, thus maintaining the overall direction of the enterprise whilst allowing individual parts of it to respond rapidly and flexibly to local needs in innovative, experimental ways. In this new world managers will be expected to act locally and rapidly, whilst continuing to think strategically, nationally and perhaps even globally.

Summary

Whilst the basic change process is deceptively straightforward, it poses a number of dilemmas for those who have to lead an organisation through a period of change. There are no simple answers, balances have to be struck, without compromising principles. A number of these dilemmas have their roots in the need to reconcile the needs of the organisation and the individuals who work for it.

Chapter 4 | THE CHANGE PROCESS

The reasonable man adapts himself to the world: the unreasonable one persists in trying to adapt the world to himself. Therefore all progress depends on the unreasonable man.

George Bernard Shaw

Lead kindly light, amid the encircling gloom, lead thou me on, the night is dark and I am far from home, I do not ask to see the distant scene; one step enough for me.

Cardinal Newman

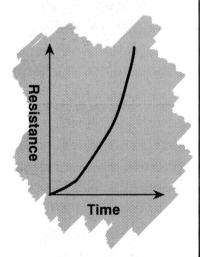

The following approach is the logical way to tackle change:

(i)   Devise an overall strategy.
(ii) Turn the strategy into a plan.
(iii) Seek sanction from those in authority.
(iv) Implement the plan.

This process wrongly assumes that man is entirely a rational creature, who will therefore accept a well reasoned, well presented argument. If he resists, opposition can be overcome by use of authority - by pressure from on high. Again wrongly, the assumption is often made that the existing organisation has the competence and capacity to work up the new arrangements.

However, experience shows that straightforward, linear processes rarely work. The strategy setting and planning processes take time, induce suspicion in those not involved and then generate a workload that feels overwhelming. This produces the maximum resistance. The concrete plan all too often allows minimal opportunity to generate commitment which would result from involvement in decision making. There is little room left for experimentation, which would lead to individual and organisational learning. In order to make progress, compliance is sought by manipulation, persuasion, barter or naked pressure from those with power. Delay sets in and is often fatal.

Successful change programmes are more complex and bitty and contain a number of other ingredients. These ingredients are described, sequentially, below but there is no certain sequence - sometimes C follows B follows A, sometimes Z comes first. Often luck plays a major part, although luck is perhaps better defined as the point at which vision and opportunity meet. The consultant psychiatrist and director of social services who, luckily, came across a redundant maternity home and turned it into an experimental home for care of elderly people, would have missed the opportunity, if they hadn't previously developed a shared vision of better care.

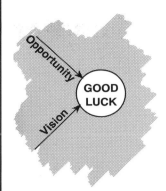

(a) Innovations

The origins of the change process can often be traced to a mass of parallel, concurrent, experimental activities. The innovative organisation builds in change as a norm, by encouraging individuals to behave entrepreneurially, - to have a go. Within reason, it allows a little anarchy. Budgets are not so tightly controlled that the organisation is in a straitjacket. Successful innovations are publicly rewarded, mistakes privately forgotten.

(b) Ice-breaking

An event, often external, often unplanned, unfreezes the situation. Griffiths recommends the introduction of general management, there is a change of government, an institutional horror story breaks, etc.

(c) Leadership, vision and strategy

The combination of these two factors, the acceptance of entrepreneurial behaviour with an unfreezing event, allows leaders to assemble a strategy for change, based on the way the organisation is already moving and congruent with behavioural changes that are already growing.

(d) Change vehicles, change drivers

Once a coherent strategy is formed and shared, key individuals are empowered by it to drive the change along, using the emerging tasks as change vehicles. The vehicles provide opportunities to do things in ways which are congruent with the emerging future rather than the past.

An Organic Change Process

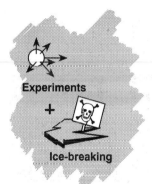

Experiments
+
Ice-breaking

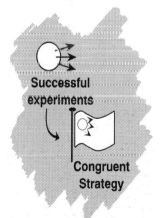

Successful experiments

Congruent Strategy

Tasks

Change Vehicles

(e) **Refreezing**

The different behaviours then become institutionalised.

This approach involves the affected people at all times. It builds on a number of small successes, rather than presenting major hurdles, which have to be jumped and which induce resistance.

The complexity and freedom of the process, however, require overall direction to ensure that the sum of this jumble of activity is purposeful. Organisations which operate successfully in this way invariably have three binding forces.

- Clarity about the overall purpose of the organisation.
- A widely shared vision about a better future.
- A set of beliefs, values and principles, which govern the way they operate.

They also have leaders.

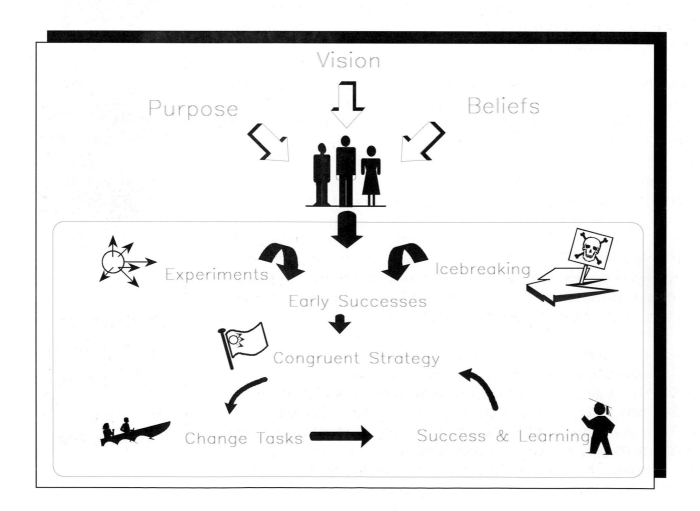

There are a number of components which will be found in most change processes. The major ones are outlined below. Detailed tools for working on them are described in the appendices.

- Clarity of core purpose
- A shared vision of a better future
- Operating principles
- Environmental constraints
- Transition management
- Resistance reduction
- Commitment planning

Elements of the Change Process

Mechanical operations can be viewed as closed systems. Things are put into them, changes take place and things come out. A lathe transforms a piece of oak into the gate-leg of a table, a refinery transforms crude oil into petrol, naphtha, fuel oil and gas. The purpose of these mechanical systems can be precisely defined.

Their effectiveness and efficiency can be measured by using these inputs and outputs to monitor the quality, quantity and cost of the desired transformation. It is tempting to use similar models for human activity systems but these are more complex and the closed system model provides an inadequate description of them[1].

A more useful model has been developed which regards each system as part of a larger one. The systems are described in terms of their core purposes. The boundaries between them are viewed as being semi-permeable. Exchanges take place across the boundaries between one system and another. The environment of the system makes demands, the system responds. This model is described as an open system.

As the model exists only in our minds, the first difficulty is that every one of us has, through our different experiences, developed a different view of the world. We therefore interpret systems differently. A teaching hospital might be seen to have a number of core purposes, e.g.:

- An institution where ill people are cured
- An institution for developing new treatments
- An institution for training student doctors and nurses
- An institution for carrying out research into disease
- A place which provides interesting employment for its staff
- A centre for the promotion of health
- A centre of excellence that provides special care not available through normal district hospitals

The Core Purpose of the Organisation

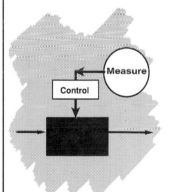

The Environment

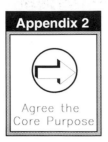

Appendix 2

Agree the
Core Purpose

A hospital can clearly be all of these but if it is to maintain a sense of direction, especially during times of change, then it needs to have one overriding core purpose, which is distinctive. This will guide its staff, enabling them to set priorities and allocate resources. If there isn't consensus on that prime purpose, if the organisation cannot answer the question "what are we here for?" with a reasonable degree of unanimity, then chaos is inevitable.

A Shared Vision of the Future

It is the shared vision of a better future which is the powerhouse of change. A piece of steel in which the component molecules are randomly arranged is just an inert lump of metal. If all the molecules are aligned in the same direction, a powerful magnet is created, capable of magical things.

In an inert steel bar the molecules are randomly arranged.

Line them up and the bar becomes a powerful magnet.

Organisations are the same. If everyone is pointing in the same direction it is magical. Nothing seems impossible.

Appendix 4

A helicopter view

Vision of
the Future

Visions are not generated by decree; they are, however, the result of leadership. It may be useful to write them on the wall but more importantly they need to be writ large in the behaviour of the organisation's leaders. In the words of Edmund Burke, "The men of England, the men, I mean, of light and leading in England, whose wisdom is open and direct, would be ashamed, as of a silly deceitful trick, to profess any religion in name, which , by their proceedings, they appeared to condemn."

Random Emmision

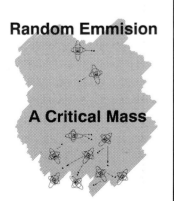

A Critical Mass

Visions need to be shared. One person alone cannot bring about change because the energy of one person can be dissipated too easily. It's a little like a single uranium atom, which radiates neutrons continuously but the neutrons escape harmlessly into space. If there is sufficient uranium around, the escaping neutrons are captured by other uranium atoms. Each captured neutron produces two more, each burst of energy releases more, until the chain reaction becomes self-sustaining and the system explodes. The mass of uranium required to produce the self-sustaining reaction is called its critical mass. Change requires a critical mass of visionary supporters if it is to become self-sustaining.

These are organisational values which will guide individuals through the maze of complex and often conflicting choices. They are something to hang on to, things which make Joe Bloggs PLC different from Lower Caldersfield DHA. They can be as blunt as Delta Airlines, "there will be no layoffs", as human as one DHA's, "we believe all our employees should be given the opportunity of doing a challenging, rewarding job". They may once have been novel, "the provision of nursing [of the elderly physically disabled] will be conducted with the minimum of interference in the personal freedom and privacy of the patient" or "all members of staff shall be treated with equal respect". They may even seem eccentric, "work will be designed to be fun". They perhaps should be obvious but need stating like the garage's "we are employed by the customers, they deserve more than our contempt". (For customers read patients?)

Today, every organisation sits in a complex environment, which we have been arguing is turbulent now and likely to become more so. Even in the somewhat simpler commercial world, organisations can no longer take the simplistic view of merely being responsible to their owners, the shareholders. Every organisation has an increasing number of people and groups who believe they have a legitimate right to interfere in the running of the enterprise. Many have and even if their right is debatable, their behaviour can still be real and disruptive. Most HAs would include the following major stakeholders and probably many more.

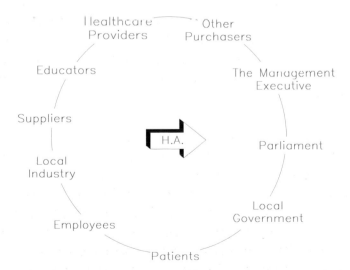

As well as the stakeholders, there are a number of other environmental domains which will also require handling; even abstractions like legislation, models of care, patterns of disease, information systems and so on. Many managers are understandably overfaced by this complexity and resort to operating in a reactive manner, dealing with problems as they arise. Effective, innovating organisations keep in touch with their environment and engage with it; attempting, at least in part, to shape it to their needs. Inevitably there are more environmental domains than time to manage them and choices have to be made. Where is the relationship already satisfactory? Where can we turn our back on it temporarily and be reasonably sure it won't bite us? Which relationship must be right if our change programme is to be successful? What are the demands and responses that currently occur between the organisation and a particular domain? What are the desirable ones? By answering these questions it is usually possible to end up with half a dozen key domains, which are especially relevant to the change being considered and to identify work that needs to be done with them.

Future, Present and Transition States

In any change process there are three states, where you are (the current state), where you want to be (the desired future state) and the bit in the middle, the transition state. The first thing to recognise is that all three states require managing and represent work, more work than the current state did by itself.

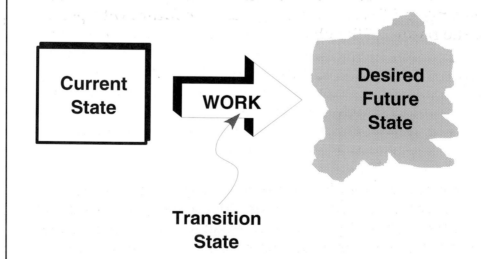

Changing the way we do things is in itself work - work which is different from and in addition to that of keeping the organisation going. This statement is so obvious that it shouldn't need to be made but I make it *ad nauseam* because so many people ignore it. Whether it is a matter of modifying the existing organisation or building a new social architecture, there will be a need for extra capacity during the change; it is not just a matter of using existing resources differently, unless the organisation has been operating with a surplus, but of providing more. Commissioning a new hospital is so obviously different from running the old one, that organisations allocate people to commissioning teams, as a matter of course. Commissioning a different management organisation in a different management style is probably a more daunting task and it also requires project management; yet people tack it onto the work of busy, current state managers. These managers certainly haven't the undivided time, they often don't have the right skills and are operating with systems designed for the current state, not the future or even the transition.

"General managers have neither the time nor the motivation to work on obsoleting what they are managing". Not a quotation from a DGM rehearsing his excuses prior to contract renewal but an observation from Peter Drucker, in *People and Performance.* Lesson one about introducing innovation must therefore be to allocate resources to the change effort. Manage the introduction of a different organisation as you would anything else. Provide change managers, allocate time and money, don't expect the existing managers to take it on as a spare time activity. If it isn't sufficiently important to warrant spending money, it isn't important enough to succeed.

Bearing in mind that much of change management is crystal ball gazing and that no one can guess the future with precision, the nature of the change needs to be understood with as much clarity as possible, so that the work of making the change can be defined and the required quantity and quality of people allocated to it. Time needs to be given to working up a description of what success will look like when it is achieved. The present then needs to be analysed and understood so that comparisons can be drawn.

There are many possible choices of management arrangements for transition management. The general manager may take on the task, if it is important enough. If he does, someone else will need to pick up some, or all, of his current state duties. A full time project manager may be justified. Project teams may be formed, built of representatives from the groups most involved in the change. Teams, sliced diagonally from across the hierarchy, can have their attractions - particularly if the aim is to shift the organisation to a more collegiate style. It may be possible to build in commitment by using natural leaders as part of the transition manage-

---

Transition Management Choices

General Manager
Project Manager
Project Teams
Representatives
Diagonal Slices
Future State Managers
Participants

ment team; the respected nurse, the senior surgeon, who will carry their colleagues with them. It is often good practise to involve designated future-state managers in transition management. They have the most compelling reasons for getting it right. Similarly, a participative approach, involving the people most affected by the change, may be time consuming, but, at worst, reduces resistance to change. At best it can add new dimensions and lead to the recognition of new opportunities. One danger is that the desired future state is so different from the present that the organisation not only finds difficulty handling the transition but is unable to stabilise the future state and the organisation therefore regresses. After all, it knows how to handle the past, all its systems were set up to do so. Regression is most common when change has been imposed as a result of crisis or with pressure from above. When the crisis is resolved or the pressure is diverted by other problems elsewhere, the organisation slips back into its old systems. It may be better to settle for a larger number of smaller step changes, each of which can be institutionalised before moving on.

Resistance to Change - Individual & Systemic

The Nadler model of organisations can be used to understand organisational behaviour during the transition process. It considers organisations as four inter-related factors which are described in more depth in chapter 5; the formal organisational arrangements, the informal culture, the individuals who work for it and the tasks it performs.

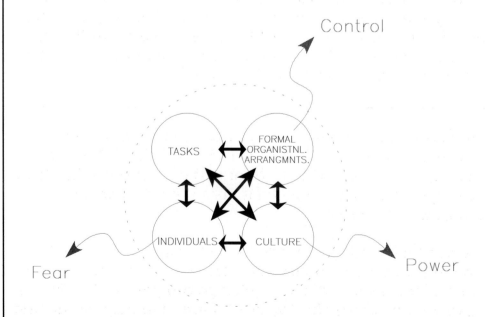

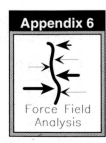

Appendix 6

Force Field
Analysis

Individuals

Individuals often resist change because of **fear** of the un-
known. They know how to cope with the way things are but
who knows whether they will be able to cope with the uncertainties of a different future? The subject of individuals in
change is so crucial that it warrants a later chapter in its
own right but the key factors for managers to work on are
two way communication and involvement.

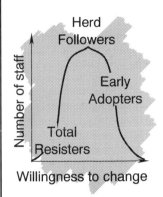

The formal organisational arrangements

The systems of the organisation were established yesterday.
When tomorrow begins to arrive, the formal organisation
finds that it is losing its monitoring capability and normally
responds by trying to regain **control**. It is the time when top
people ask for "brief", written additional reports from the
change managers, who are usually already overloaded.

The informal organisation

The informal organisation's basic concern is power. The
uncertainty and ambiguity of change tend to lead to political
behaviour as groups worry about the balance of **power** and
how the change will affect their own positions. Power to get
things done can also disappear, as informal networks are
destroyed.

There is a danger that the organisation can become triply
incompetent. The formal systems become less appropriate,
the informal arrangements which cover the gaps in the formal system fragment and individuals do not have the skills
or the motivation to pick up the pieces.

Commitment planning is an essential ingredient of any
change programme. Who needs to be on board? Who will
make up the critical mass? What is their current attitude to
the proposed changes and what does it need to be if the
change is to succeed?

Having identified key individuals and groups, what can be
done to gain their commitment? The key people may not be
aware of the issues which the change programme is address-
ing therefore *openly sharing* this information may be the first
step. Activities which allow them to recognise and acknowledge problems, without public loss of face, can be useful.
Joint problem-solving is perhaps the most successful way of

Seeking Commitment

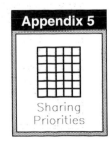

Appendix 5

Sharing
Priorities

Appendix 7

A+B+C>D

Change
Equation

engaging their interest - getting alongside them and treating their hurting systems often provides a foundation for later work. Altering the *reward systems* can be essential. If, on the one hand, the organisation is trying to shift towards community care but measures the unit's performance in terms of bed occupation, change is less than likely. *Educational activities* can often be sufficiently neutral to be acceptable. Finally, *role modelling* by senior individuals can be a very powerful way of changing behaviour: it isn't a coincidence that courteous clinical consultants tend to have considerate registrars.

Characteristics of Change

Change is characteristically uncertain. It is resource intensive, generates conflict and polarises opinions. It crosses organisational boundaries and presents new unforeseen alternatives.

Change is helped by:	Change is hindered by:
Faith, imagination, vision	Elaborate analysis/forecasting
Leadership	Invariant procedures
Patience and persistence	Expectations of rapidity
Planned flexibility	Tight targets
Stable working teams	Career moves of key people
Release from current work	Change work not recognised
Committed people	Assigned Staff
Intense, focused activities	Organisational distractions
Multi-disciplinary work	Specialisation
Horizontal trading	Linear hierarchies
Boundary management	Professional tribes

References

1. Peter Checkland, *Systems Thinking, Systems Practise*, Wiley 1981

2. R. Kanter, *The Change Masters*, Counterpoint 1983

Approaching the New Millennium (1993 Edition)

The fundamental constituents of the change process have not altered - shared principles, an agreed vision, commitment to a common mission, leadership, involvement and hard purposeful work are still as essential as ever. However, they can no longer guarantee survival. The average levels of environmental turbulence are now so high that, for many of us, organisational and personal survival will depend on achieving new levels of flexibility - on increasing our capacity to respond to the totally unexpected. However, the NHS is still a broad church. Some parts continue to operate in surprisingly stable surroundings. In such circumstances, all that is needed is the competent, reliable, repetitive delivery of an effective, efficient service. For some, the world is changing in an entirely predictable way - perhaps at an alarming rate but still in ways which can be handled by an extrapolation of previous experience. For some, whilst trends can be identified, they present new challenges outside our previous experience- the change has become discontinuous. At the extreme, for some, tomorrow is entirely unpredictable - managing change has become a matter of identifying surprises early and responding rapidly to them. The change process that an organisation adopts will depend on its situation. Those facing a stable environment will rightly continue to forecast and plan, budget and control. As the turbulence increases, so will the need for strategic change management. At some point it may well be necessary to develop alternative visions, painting several scenarios to match different views of possible futures - scenario planning. Those at the extreme, for example in the realms of genetics and computing, will need to establish formal methods for scanning their horizons, identifying novel shifts early, deciding which are important and actively managing and modifying their change strategy to meet the changing circumstances.

Igor Ansoff has written extensively on the problems of Strategic Management and in Implanting Strategic Management, Ansoff and McDonnell, Prentice Hall 1990, summarises the issues involved in responding to discontinuous environmental change.

Summary

Change is unpredictable and can be over-managed into extinction. Change strategies based on entrepreneurial innovation which take advantages of ice-breaking events generate less resistance and incur less delay than over-planned grand strategies. There are common features to most change programmes which can be worked on and which increase the likelihood of successful, stabilised transitions. The commonest failing is to allocate insufficient resources to managing the transition state.

Chapter 5 | A HEALTHY, INNOVATIVE ORGANISATION

On the stage, masks are assumed with some regard to procedure: in everyday life, the participants act their parts without consideration for the suitability of the scene or for the words spoken by the rest of the cast: the result is a general tendency for things to be brought to the level of farce even when the theme is serious enough.

Anthony Powell, "A Dance to the Music of Time"

He is a barbarian, and thinks that the customs of his tribe are the laws of nature.

George Bernard Shaw

The organisational form which has dominated twentieth century industrial society has undoubtedly been the bureaucracy. The NHS is a bureaucracy and if we are to succeed in introducing change within the service, whatever the nature of that change, it would be foolish to deny the bureaucratic history of the organisation. The question which must be addressed is whether that basic structure will inevitably remain unchanged, whether it can and should be modified or whether the age of bureaucracy is past and we have to learn to work in a totally new structure. The prophets of major change have been arguing, for the last twenty to thirty years, that the death of the bureaucracies, as we have known them, is imminent. Tofler[1] vividly paints the nightmare of "each man frozen into a narrow, unchanging niche in a rabbit-warren bureaucracy. The walls of this niche squeeze the individuality out of him, smash his personality and compel him, in effect, to conform or die." He goes on to argue that we are seeing the emergence of a "free-form world of kinetic organisations".

The need for organisational reshaping was forecast, on humanist grounds, in the fifties, by sociologists such as McGregor[2] and it is perhaps perverse that organisations moving towards different structures are now doing so for very different reasons. The drive to introduce new organisational styles comes more from matching the organisation to the technology of the sunrise industries, the rebirth of small organisations, the increasing concern with effectiveness and efficiency, the drive for decentralisation and the explosion of information technology, the move to an international society and the consequent need to reshape our multinational companies - as well as the need to handle competition from highly successful Japanese style organisations. Above all, organisations are recognising the need to develop systems which can handle the accelerating rate of change. The prime characteristic of an effective bureaucracy is that it requires the world to be reasonably predictable. The continuing uncertainty of today's world is the challenge that bureaucracies face.

Before examining some of these questions in more detail, what is an organisation? For a start, it is worth remembering the accepted wisdom that every enterprise has four organisations; the one that is written down, the one that most people believe exists, the one that really exists and, finally, the one that the enterprise really needs.

The organisation is also clearly more than its formal arrangements. Nadler[5] described this issue in some detail and the following model captures the core of his argument, although it has been modified based on experience working in the NHS.

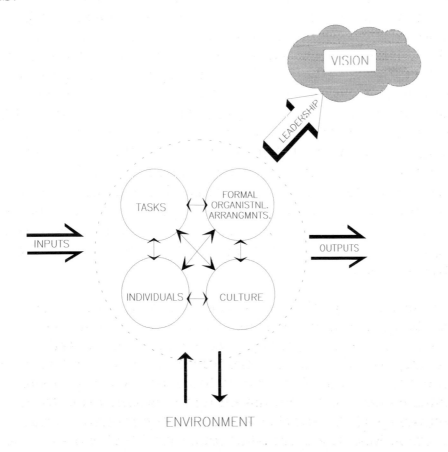

The Formal Organisational Arrangements

These are hard. They can usually be written down on paper and typically would include organisation charts, lines of accountability, policies, operating instructions, budgets, formal meeting and committee structures, job descriptions, pay and reward procedures, information systems, monitoring and control mechanisms.

Because the formal arrangements have been devised to meet the needs of the organisation as it was yesterday, they rarely completely match the needs of today and tomorrow. It is a common experience in large organisations to find that even the very basic information is out of date. Technology has changed but the operating procedures haven't been modified, yet. The formal organisation charts match the last but one reorganisation. When I first started work, organisation charts were printed on glossy paper and displayed on the wall with a certain degree of performance. Today they are more often written in pencil or lost in a drawer. It's perhaps a sign of their increasingly ephemeral nature.

The Culture

This sector of the model is less tangible but it is the mix of things that gives the organisation meaning for those who work in it. It includes the lubricants that make the formal structure work and it looks after the difference between yesterday's written instructions and today's reality. It includes the culture, the major values of the organisation, such as Marks and Spencer's commitment to Quality Assurance, ICI's (past?) concern with elegant, technical solutions, British Airways' worry over putting people first. But it also includes the rites and rituals, the individual values that humanise the organisation, the way things get done around here, the normal, informal rewards and punishments. It's about who you know; it is about horse-trading. It includes the way people dress and how they address each other, the acceptable levels of openness, honesty and trust in their communications. It is about allegiances and alliances, tribalism, professionalism and loyalties.

Whilst at times of change the formal organisational arrangements focus on authority, the informal is concerned with power.

Individuals

People come and go. Each brings to the organisation different skills and knowledge, different views of the world, different experience, different attitudes, different values, different personalities. Whilst the formal organisational arrangements tend to assume that people can be matched with reasonable precision to prescribed jobs, in reality a balance is always struck. Individuals make choices about how they will tackle the job, in part shaping their behaviour to suit the formal and informal organisation, in part adapting the structure to meet their personal needs. The degree of freedom varies with the overall organisational style but no two people tackle the same job in exactly the same way.

Tasks

The organisation exists in order to pursue some purposeful human activity, the prime reason for which the organisation exists. The tasks should be inextricably linked to furthering the cause - to supporting the central transformation. Organisations have a nasty habit of generating tasks which consume a vast amount of organisational energy internally but which have little impact on the organisation's external effectiveness.

The four elements exist in a state of dynamic equilibrium between themselves and with their environment. In healthy organisations, as one element changes the others shift to accommodate. At times of overall change, each tends to resist the change with a degree of predictability (cf. chapter 4). The major point, however, is that change leaders need to work with all four elements if they are to succeed. The NHS's concern with the formal structures is obvious. Its interest in some of the other sectors has not always been as apparent.

The Healthy Organisation

Before looking at organisational choices, it is worth noting that, irrespective of an organisation's particular arrangements, there are a number of features which can be used to check its overall health. Peters[3] refined these into five. The excellent organisation treats its *customers*, in our case the public, with respect, care and consideration. It is constantly *innovative*, looking for new ideas, better ways of achieving excellent performance. It *empowers its people*. It is populated by *leaders who love change*. Its systems are robust but focused on delivery - *upside down systems*. It may be that it is tacitly included in the above but in today's climate I would also add, explicitly, they have a healthy respect for *money*. This has been ingrained in me ever since I was involved with a group of senior industrial managers defining the characteristics of a good manager, as an aid to recruitment. No manager mentioned profit, everyone later explained that they took it for granted. The following year, the organisation made a loss of £100,000,000.

Older, well tried models suggest the following description of health.

The organisation is purposeful
Healthy organisations know where they are going, they have an overall shared vision of the future and a set of goals that they work towards.

Leadership is visible
The senior managers spend a substantial part of their time in direct contact with their staff, at all levels - setting directions, monitoring performance, helping fight fires, persuading and motivating.

Structure matches strategy
The way the organisation is set up matches its purpose. The structure is also sufficiently flexible to meet the changes that the organisation faces. (This is often written as "form follows function", a phrase borrowed from the world of architecture. I sometimes wonder whether major shifts in architecture, both of buildings and organisations, don't owe something to free experiments in new forms? Can function follow form?)

Decisions are made at the lowest appropriate level
Decision making is based on availability of information rather than status and hierarchical position. Information flows freely and horizontally, as well as vertically.

Rewards are linked to achievement
Achievements are recognised and rewarded, both formally and informally. Managers acknowledge success and tolerate mistakes, but never the same one twice.

Communication is open
People can contribute ideas and opinions, suggest goals and comment on behaviour. Conflict is managed not suppressed.

The organisation is grounded in reality
Changes are monitored; there is a conscious attempt to obtain feedback; individuals want to know the consequences of their actions; perceptions are tested.

The organisation manages its boundaries
It sees itself as part of a larger system. The exchange with other systems is managed proactively.

Above all it is a learning organisation

Our service is so varied and complex that it would be foolish to attempt an overall diagnosis of the state of its health against any list. Like most, it probably resembles the curate's egg, good in parts. If I were to risk one comment it would be that we have all heard stories of staff who wouldn't know their office-bound managers, if they passed them in the street, have never met them and have no idea of what they are about, what they are trying to do. If this were true, would it be surprising if the district nurse, struggling to cope with an increasing number of elderly patients, saw your cherished change programme as yet another irrelevant exercise in "management" for "them up there"?

Happily, it isn't necessary to look outside the NHS for examples of excellent practise. For example, I once came across a rather shattered personnel officer who was involved in seeing more than a thousand ancillary staff, individually, to ensure that they understood the ins and outs of competitive tendering and how it might affect them financially. He was concerned that any decisions they took should be based on the right information for their own circumstances and felt that the service owed them this courtesy. "A belief in people" in action.

Appendix 1

The
Healthy
Organisation

The NHS has embarked on many, major, nationwide change programmes. The outcomes have not always been evaluated but too often it feels that the time and resources consumed have been more than anticipated and the level of success less than desired. Why? There are no doubt many reasons but one I would suspect is a preoccupation with establishing and approving structures, a preoccupation with getting the structure right; a preoccupation which seems to place the formal organisational arrangements pre-eminent in the strategy for bringing about major organisational change. The bureaucratic concern with structure is deeply ingrained in the service. I remember one intense discussion about the proper distribution of responsibilities between units and districts, which centred around who should be responsible for level 4 activities. A comment that this made a number of fundamental assumptions about the type of organisation needed was briefly acknowledged and then totally ignored!

Does the NHS need to be bureaucratic or are alternative organisational styles possible, desirable or even essential? If

Alternatives to Bureaucracies

we acknowledge the variety and relative independence of the bits that make up the NHS, there can be no one prescriptive answer but the question needs to be repeatedly asked. Do we need to make fundamental changes in the fabric of our organisation, if we are to survive into the 21st. century?

It may be that many hospitals are mature organisations, largely concerned with delivering a relatively constant repertoire of behaviour, efficiently and effectively and that the bureaucratic form fundamentally suits them. Financial pressures may however force them to look for shifts in behaviour which enable them to be more responsive, more efficient and more effective making modifications which introduce flexibility but still retain the overall bureaucratic form? In some hospitals, the increasing reliance on clinical directorates, in one form or another, could signal the shift to a more collegiate approach.

If the next fifteen years sees a continuing shift towards community care, what organisational style will be appropriate for the more community-based services? The tasks of the community organisation are likely to be sufficiently different to justify a "green field site" approach. What kind of organisation can span health authorities, family practitioners, social services, volunteers, relatives and friends, in order to provide decent community care for the elderly, the mentally handicapped and the mentally ill? Bureaucracies seem inappropriate. If non-bureaucratic solutions are adopted for one, increasingly vital, bit of the organisation and not for the rest, how does the centre cope?

What alternative organisations are there? One way of describing organisations is to place them on two axes, which describe their degree of systematisation and centralisation[6]. Organisations which are both highly centralised and highly systematic we call bureaucratic; centralised but unsystematic, autocratic; decentralised and unsystematic, anarchic. The combination of systematic and yet decentralised is the fluid, emerging organisation which is sometimes described as a matrix, to emphasise its mixture of horizontal and vertical organisational links. Matrix organisations have lately been receiving a bad press because of the confusion the very formal matrices can produce. The terms collegiate or project based are perhaps better as they infer the way groups form and reform around the changing tasks, where the pass key to join a particular club is competent commitment. All of these terms can be used pejoratively: "autocrats are self seeking", "bureaucrats are stuffy" etc. They are used here neutrally; autocracy, bureaucracy and even anarchy, all have their place.

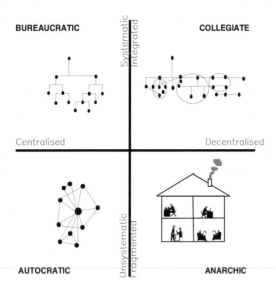

Most organisations in their infancy are autocratic, in the sense that they owe their shape and values to one individual, the entrepreneur who founded the enterprise. They focus heavily on the boss and his values. There is no need for structure and systems; employees just need to put themselves in the boss's shoes and do things the way he would. They can thus operate away from base, with the minimum of apparent controls, and considerable freedom to make decisions. These organisations value soft data, opinions, verbal communication. Reward for achievement is usually more work, increased responsibility, trust and more challenge. Autocracies are able to tolerate considerable uncertainty as long as they remain small enough for the communication networks to be maintained.

Autocratic Organisations

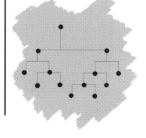

Bureaucratic organisations are essentially formal and there is usually a strong emphasis on structure. "One person has one boss and two subordinates, and so on, unto the seventh generation". They have developed as efficient ways of controlling mature, large organisations. Jobs are described in writing and the job descriptions determine pay and reward systems. Logic rules, policies are debated, plans are made in orderly cycles and necessarily precede implementation. Bids

Bureaucratic Organisations

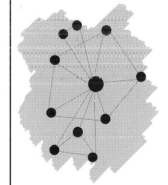

are made for resources, overtly using rational systems although covertly internal politics can be rife. Performance is measured numerically and control mechanisms tend to be uniform, in order to allow organisation-wide comparisons to be made centrally. Written communication is valued and subjective views are not welcomed. Promotion is the normal reward and can become an end in its own right. The organisation values certainty and has difficulty tolerating ambiguity.

One of the dangers of bureaucracies is neatly summarised in a jingle which is to be found on many a reluctant bureaucrat's wall:

> "Along this tree
> From root to crown
> Ideas flow up
> And vetoes down"

Anarchic Organisations

People work in these organisations and not for them. Typically they would include solicitors' partnerships, general practice and some academic institutions. There is a perceived need to share some minimal organisational resources - a building, secretaries, expensive equipment, but there are few common goals. Individuality is valued above all else. There is little organisational authority; the academics insist on their tenure, the GPs on their clinical freedom. I am told that few solicitors draw up formal contracts for their own partnerships, which makes life difficult if they fall out. Standards are set professionally and outside interference is resented. Rewards are found in the job itself or in professional recognition from peers.

Project-based (Collegiate) Organisations

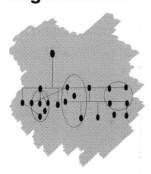

In project based organisations, whilst individuals may have functional bosses who are responsible for their individual competence and often for their career development, they work for a significant part of their time in teams, based around particular tasks. The teams may have no long term existence, often they form to handle a particular project and then disband. The NASA space project in its early days was largely managed in this way. Individuals are valued above all for their competence. It is common for one individual to have several bosses. The production manager may be responsible to the production director for the performance and safety of his plant. He may also lead a team looking at novel manufacturing techniques and be responsible to the research director for this activity, whilst spending part of his time working with a new business group who call on his expert production knowledge from time to time. These organisations typically see achievement as the main reward. They value variety and tolerate ambiguity and change. In their more extreme forms, they are completely fluid and form the basis for the innovative skunk works of Peters and Waterman.[3] They can be close to bureaucracies, when an overlay of temporary project teams is used to break down some of the undesirable compartmentalism of vertical hierarchies. The decision-making style is typically participative, ideas flow from all parts of the organisation but the organisations are predominantly "bottom-up".

Are some of the answers to designing community based organisations to be found in the project based approach? Can we learn some lessons from other organisations about building innovation into our bureaucracies without, necessarily, destroying them?

What can be done to encourage innovation and change? Comparisons have shown[4] that innovative organisations differ from less innovative ones in a number of key ways:

Building in Innovation

More innovative	Less innovative
Change is normal	Change is a shock
Organisation at least partially collegiate	Organisation hierarchical and bureaucratic
Free flow of information	Information flow constrained
Numerous horizontal connections	Vertical communication dominated
Clear set of cultural beliefs	Idiosyncratic
Pride in the organisation	Uncertainty and confusion
Abundant rewards (visibility, more challenging work, bigger projects)	Scarce rewards grudgingly given

Where does this lead in terms of possible first steps? Four ways of exploring the project based approach could be to:

Eliminate unnecessary layers

If bureaucratic layers get in the way of communication reduce them. What does a particular level add to the organisation which is distinctive or additive? If the answer is nothing, eliminate it. Establish mechanisms which cross the layers, build teams from diagonal slices. Think the unthinkable, by-pass people, set up situations where junior staff work with the most senior.

Build horizontal linkages

Establish *small*, cross functional, change project teams, with project managers. Write a remit for the team and publish it widely, base the membership on the ability to contribute skills, resources and competence, not on professional representation. Put a closure date on their activities. Demand results, expect mistakes, implement their ideas and publicise success. Make them accountable to someone with clout, who can also get them the resources they need. Exchange people, move the successful innovator to another project in another department. Use task forces to solve problems, explore opportunities.

Improve the sideways flow of information

Establish briefing groups which bring together several layers of the hierarchy - brief in task groups. Share ideas, thoughts on new directions, whilst they are still at the formative stage. Use the power of the computer to make information available. Establish mechanisms for sharing ideas: Quality Circles used to be called work group discussions before they went to Japan, but the basic idea of asking those who have hands on experience and who work together to meet regularly and seek better ways of doing things, is powerful. Make sure they have access to any information they want.

Establishing learning systems linked to change

Our training systems are usually set up to maintain the organisation the way it is, to provide "more of ...", "replacements for" ... or "improvements to ...". Our traditional performance appraisal schemes commonly aim to identify and rectify the gap between desired and actual performance and to question the potential of individuals using the yardstick of today's enterprise; all against organisational maintenance goals. Instead, establish learning programmes which encourage the exploration of new skills. How do other people in other organisations handle their problems? What are the skills we need to meet our best guesses about tomorrow? Set up exercises to learn from things that go well. Encourage people to extend their horizons, to take time out to understand the future and put their plans alongside the future rather than the present.

I remember working with a group of NHS general managers who were thinking about the kind of organisation they wished to create in their district. The language they used was infectious: they wanted to work in an organisation that was task-based, patient-centred, innovative, risk taking, imaginative, effective and efficient, flexible and organic, responsive, both internally and externally, adult rather than paternalistic, managerial rather than professional and above all concerned for its clients and its staff. Despite the obvious reservations about the enormous size of the task of making it happen compared to the relative ease of imagining it, the vision was clear and clearly not bureaucratic. The reservations that then began to emerge had something to do with problems with the porters, trouble with competitive tendering and overspending back at the ranch. Is dreaming dreams cloud cuckoo land or is it an essential ingredient in the change process?

References

1. Alvin Tofler, *Future Shock*, Bodley Head 1970.

2. D. McGregor, *The Human Side of Enterprise*, McGraw-Hill 1960

3. T. Peters and N. Austin, *A Passion for Excellence*, Collins 1985

4. Rosabeth Kanter, *The Change Masters*, Counterpoint 1983

5. D. Nadler and M. L. Tushman; A model for diagnosing organisational behaviour; *Organisational Dynamics*, Autumn 1980. AMA.

6. The author first came across this concept from P. Smith of Ashridge College. It is developed comprehensively in *The Gods of Management* by C. Hardy.

Approaching the New Millennium (1993) Edition.

Striking the appropriate balance of organisational style still bedevils the Service and the consequences can be harsh, particularly for those who work at its boundaries. In an environment subject more and more to market forces, many provider unit managers recognise, intellectually, that their salvation lies in building organisations that focus on and delegate responsibility to groups of clinical specialties which are then encouraged to operate in a robust and systematic way - the very essence of project based management - devolution plus systematic integration. Making such a culture shift in organisations which have often encompassed a whole range of styles is inevitably a medium to long term strategy. Tasks have to be reallocated, power redistributed, individuals have to adopt new attitudes and develop additional skills. Nevertheless, the same managers are expected to balance the books and deliver major improvements in service immediately and may even find their performance monitored in old fashioned bureaucratic ways. Despite the fact that bureaucracies are collapsing world wide, the temptation to impose tight centralised bureaucratic control must be very great. It will be a brave general manager who whole-heartedly commits the organisation to a new and perhaps unproven approach. The career pitfalls of doing so and then failing are obvious to all. The problem is that anything less than complete commitment may well guarantee failure.

Summary

The organisation provides the framework within which change takes place. Bureaucracy has been the traditional organisational form by which large enterprises have been run. Bureaucracies have difficulty managing rapid change. Are there other more appropriate forms for the future of our organisation? Do we at least need to modify some bureaucratic habits if we are to become sufficiently innovative to survive into the 21st century?

ADMINISTRATORS, MANAGERS OR LEADERS?

Chapter 6

One man that has a mind and knows it can always beat ten men who haven't and don't.

George Bernard Shaw

In real life the most practical advice for leaders is not to treat pawns like pawns, nor princes like princes, but all persons like persons.

J.M. Burns

Eh! je suis leur chef, il fallait bien les suivre.

Alexandre Rollin

Administration or Management- What's the Difference?

To begin at the beginning, what do we mean by the terms administration and management and how are they related to leadership? How important are any of them to change and innovation? Some people and most dictionaries use the first two as if they were interchangeable and perhaps we are all prone to making sweeping statements about the world needing more leadership, without thinking carefully of what we mean and why it is appropriate in a given situation. How much of each do we need in the NHS now and in the next ten years? This is not mere pedantry. If, as is implied by changes in the management arrangements, administration, management and leadership are distinctly different and require different behaviours, this has significant implications for allocation of resources and for selection, education and development processes. How does a panel select a unit general manager, if it isn't totally in agreement about which of the three beasts it is looking for? From experience, I would say with difficulty and I would suspect that lengthy job descriptions and short pre-interview conversations don't solve the problem.

The dictionary definition of administration is less than helpful in drawing distinctions.   Administration is usually described as the management of a business, a public service or an estate. What of the music rather than the words? Administration carries with it the flavour of stability, orderliness, structure - a well oiled machine; of administrators providing advice to the policy-makers and then ensuring that the policy-makers' decisions are implemented with the minimum of fuss. The NHS model might be one in which administration is basically seen as a supporting mechanism to help medical, nursing and similar staff go about the real business of the service, with the minimum of interference. Rosemary Stewart's study of the NHS administrators[7] describes how, despite a wide variety of behaviour, the DAs and Area Administrators of the time saw themselves as enablers, organisers, coordinators, team builders, educators and spokesmen but rarely as innovators.

What are managers? Enough has been written about management to fill many libraries, from the time when Fayol[8] described management as the process of planning, organising, commanding, coordinating and controlling to today's literature, which seems to be more about creating champions or doing callisthenics whilst wearing overalls, depending upon whether you favour the American or the Japanese version. Why so much study and theorising? In Peter Checkland's words[5] "We find ourselves for a brief span inhabiting a mysterious universe. We have an itch, a need to try to understand it." What is it all about? The scientific approach to such intriguing questions, based on the philosophy of Rene Descartes, led western society to approach complex problems by breaking them up into their component parts; science into physics, chemistry and biology; chemistry into organic, inorganic and physical, and so on until it became possible, as epitomised in the Hitch-hikers' Guide to the Galaxy, to know a lot of highly specialised answers but perhaps to have forgotten the basic question? Management is more of an art than a science but management educators have followed a similar path to the scientists and, as a result, there are now thousands of studies of management in action and a confusing array of fragmented, specialised, fashionable management processes. Many managers could tell you all about MBO, performance appraisal, the management grid, level 4 etc. How many managers could answer Mintzberg's[6] naive questions, What do managers do?. What are managers for? What purpose do they serve? Why do we need them? What is their role in bringing about change? If we didn't have them what would we miss?

The pioneering work of Mintzberg, Stewart, Kotter and Lawrence[6,7,8,9,10] has led to some deceptively simple statements about what effective managers do, which many of us may find easier to accept than to practise:

(i) There is no one best way to approach the task of management. Successful managers do things differently depending on the circumstances and their own competencies, of which they are very aware.

(ii) They establish processes by which people understand the overall mission of the organisation, by which people develop and share a corporate vision and set goals.

(iii) They seek the necessary resources and ensure that scarce ones are allocated appropriately between competing demands.

(iv) They keep in close touch with what is happening inside and outside their organisation and make sure that people are well informed. To quote one senior general manager, "no one in my organisation should be surprised about tomorrow; next week yes, tomorrow no."

(v) They get staff to cooperate, getting things done despite resistance, red tape, political opposition etc.

(vi) They set the overall climate and culture; they are the architects of the social structure of the organisation.

Over-managed and Under-led?

The NHS was until the 1980s, with notable and often necessarily covert exceptions, administered rather than managed. Implementation of the Griffiths' report produced an overt move towards more management as summarised above but, just when we were coming to terms with the different view, the kaleidoscope shifted again and we are seeing a different set of patterns emerging from the management gurus. One of the profession's leading educators takes as his theme song, "the problem with our large organisations is that they have been over-managed and under-led.[1]" Many writers are joining in the chorus[2,3,4] and talk of the crisis of leadership as being the key issue or our time. If we live in turbulent times, do you manage or lead people through change, or is it a bit of both?

Leadership - What is it?

Management and leadership are so intertwined that they can not be completely separated. It is however worth, even if somewhat artificially, distinguishing the two activities - if only to emphasise the need for more or less of the two, in different circumstances. Let me begin by taking two examples before settling on some definitions. I once spent a very happy holiday in Madeira, staying at a medium sized hotel owned by a somewhat eccentric Anglo-Portuguese lady. In between idling my time away by the pool and overindulging in the good things of life, I occasionally speculated on the hotel organisation. The owner only visited the place a few times while we were there. There was no obvious supervision, no resident manager, no operating manuals; yet all the various activities concerned with the welfare of, say, a hundred people ticked along smoothly and efficiently. I suspect there were no job descriptions or organisation charts, no performance appraisal schemes, no written core missions. Nevertheless, it was a place where people were aligned behind the enterprise. The staff didn't need to be told what to do, they worked together in harmony. If something out of the ordinary arose, they handled it. There was a basic pride in their work and in their hotel. Not once did we hear "I am sorry I can't help, I only work here." My wife, somewhat intrigued, decided to explore a little and soon discovered a wealth of stories: one will suffice as an illustration. A while back, a rather squeaky crane began operating on the docks late at night disturbing the guests' sleep. The hotel owner, a lady in her seventies, purchased a drum of lubricating oil, climbed the crane and delivered it personally to the crane driver, together with fairly explicit comments on what she would do next if he failed to apply it regularly to the offending parts. This delightful lady seemed to me to be more of a leader than a manager.

Again taking another example away from both patients and chain stores, in 1942, Sir John Barberolli undertook the daunting task of turning an organisation little better than the Manchester town band into the Halle, a symphony orchestra of international renown. Some 40 years later and 15 years after his death, members of the orchestra remembered him like this, their voices still charged with emotion ... "The thrill of it, the feeling that while it was going on it was the most important thing in the world, somehow it was all intensified to a degree that one hadn't experienced before ... " "Everything he did was geared to the Halle, it was his life .. and all the people connected with it ... he was concerned about us ... we were his family ..." "Well he was very friendly towards us until we came to the music and then we

were musicians, my goodness he used to say the most fright-
ful things. ..." "He set standards which we knew were impossible but we achieved them. ..." "You could say anything to
him if you believed it, and he wouldn't take offence, he would
always consider it." Statements about a leader not a manager[12].

J.M. Burns nicely distinguished two leadership behaviours,
transforming and transactional[11]. It is arguable that management, as we normally describe it, teach it and practise it,
follows his transactional model and that when people argue
for more leadership they are seeking to increase the level of
transformational behaviour. I am therefore going to use
Burke's[13] phrases transforming leadership and transactional
management to emphasise the difference and to argue that,
whilst both are necessary, change demands more of the
transforming style than we normally experience. Transactional management is basically a bargaining process in
which manager and managed trade. It is not the exercise of
naked power; the traders are recognised as persons, the
power of each is acknowledged and forms the basis of the
contract, the transaction. The manager aims to further the
purposes of the organisation by the nature of the contracts
he strikes. The basic bargain is one of the labourer and the
hirer. If the managed person meets the annual objectives,
however they are set, rewards follow in the shape of contin-
ued employment, promotion, increased status, more salary
etc. If the clinician makes savings, then he can spend part
of them on developing his service. If a general manager de-
livers a more efficient and effective unit, his contract will be
renewed. Transforming leaders operate at a different level.
They engage totally with their followers, in such a way that
both leader and followers are mutually empowered and moti-
vated. The purposes of the leader and the followers may
have started as separate but in the process they become
fused. A simplistic way of emphasising the difference would
be to destroy the transforming leadership of Martin Luther
King's "I have a dream ..." and substitute the classic transactional management language of "I have five key result
areas ...". More comprehensively, transforming leaders (TLs)
are emotionally involved with the institution and its aims,
they work with ideas, ideals and visions whereas Transactional managers (TMs) worry about the task and the people
associated with the task. TLs inspire and work with the
whole person, their own private life is indistinguishable from
their life at work, they hold people accountable by implicit
processes, you feel guilty if you let them down, whereas TMs
involve people, they are concerned with people only at work,

their own private life is kept private, they set up explicit contracts, for example often using management by objectives, and they just want the task accomplished. TLs are by nature stirrers, they create problems, focus on the long term, are interested in ends not means. TMs are fixers, they solve problems, concern themselves with means, focus on the short and medium term. TLs inspire their staff by expecting them to do more than they thought possible. They often approach management development by throwing people in at the deep end and then demonstrate complete confidence by walking away. However, they manage to be around when things go well, so that they can reward success, informally. They encourage mistakes but abhor failure. TMs provide feedback, coaching, planned experience and an element of sheltered learning. Emotionally, transforming leaders appreciate contrariness, they appeal to the needs of the child in all of us and inspire intense feelings from us; we identify with them or dislike them, almost love or hate them. Life with a transforming leader tends to be turbulent. Transactional managers like conformity, they appeal to our adult needs for autonomy and involvement and they generate less emotion. Life with a transactional manager is more comfortable and orderly.

Transforming Leaders	Transactional Managers
Empower	**Bargain**
Inspire by ideals, ideas, visions	Task and people centred
Whole person	Person at work
Mix work and home	Separate work and home
Implicit contracts	Explicit contracts
Stirrers	Fixers
Long term focus	Short/medium term focus
Challenge, encourage mistakes	Coach, sheltered learning
Reward informally, personally	Reward formally
Like contrariness	Like conformity
Emotional, turbulent	Comfortable, orderly
SIMPLIFY	**COMPLICATE**

Transactional managers seek to move towards order and stability and in doing so complicate life for their followers. Their tendency towards rational analysis leads to fragmentation and when change is around, the fragmentation leads to loss of vision; the wood is obscured by the trees. Transformational leaders work happily with complexity and ambiguity. In so doing, they simplify life for their followers because they operate at the level of principles and vision. They are able to keep in view the whole systems and see how each individual part fits into the total jigsaw.

The fundamental scientific law of thermodynamics states that the universe is inexorably moving towards a state of increasing disorder and complexity: perhaps that is why we feel an increasing need for more leadership and less management. Managers and management educators have tended to assume that goals are clear, alternatives known, that options can be appraised, detailed plans made and tidily implemented. Happily the world is more exciting and unpredictable. We are often not quite sure that we understand the problem and we all approach it with our own, different set of values and perceptions. The judgements we make, particularly in a service like ours, are inevitably soft and subjective, the precise goals are unclear and often in conflict with one another. Technology changes and new horizons open. The process of planning is iterative and uncertain. Leaders help us handle this uncertainty without denying its reality, which is why it is argued that change demands more leadership and less management.

Leadership in Changing Organisations

What is the leader's basic role in change? Bennis suggests (loc. cit.) that there are four main features. Notice the overlap with the previous studies of effective managers:

(i) Leaders above all have an ability to generate a vision of the desired future, to see ways in which the organisation can develop which will match changes in its environment and which at the same time are compatible with its history. They can see the emerging shape of the whole system and can gain commitment of the organisation to that whole; the vision is a shared one.

(ii) The leader is the prime social architect, the person who understands the culture of the organisation and can reshape it, can reset the norms and values, the way people act, the way decisions are taken, altering the organisational style to overcome its systemic resistance to change.

(iii) Leaders position their organisation in the environment by clarifying what business they are in, looking outward to predict changes in their environment, seeking appropriate linkages between their organisation and its environment and making internal changes to match those links.

(iv) They operate in an innovative learning style. This learning is not aimed at maintaining the organisation's ability to do the things it does well, necessary though this may be, but at helping themselves and their organisations learn to handle the newly emerging issues.

Bennis also encapsulates the leader's focus on winning, in what he christens the Wallenda factor. The late Karl Wallenda was the great tightrope walker who, on his last and fateful walk, changed the habits of a lifetime. Instead of concentrating his energies on walking the rope, he worried for three months about how to avoid falling off. Sadly the result was his death. Bennis concludes that leaders concentrate on success not on avoiding failure.

Does any of the above help to unravel one of the main change dilemmas, that is, how can organisations be top led and bottom driven simultaneously? Managers will be familiar with the Tannembaum-Schmidt continuum, below, which moves from a situation of outright manipulation (tell and sell), through to the formation of coalitions, (joining and delegating), the classical and effective solutions of the transactional manager to the dilemma.

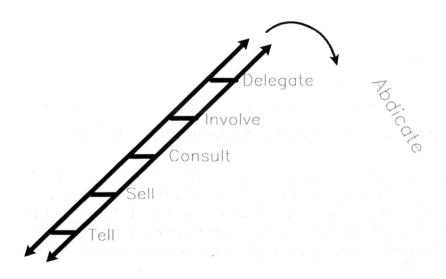

The transformational leaders operate differently. They induce followers to work towards goals that represent the values and needs of both the leader and the follower. They may exhibit different levels of motivation, skill and power from their followers; they may emphasise or even ignore some aspects of their followers' needs but there is a commonality of purpose which is not achieved by Machiavellian principles. Transformational leaders derive their power from their followers and operate by empowering their followers. The process is symbiotic, the whole is greater than the sum of its parts.

Finally, how do we measure the effectiveness of leadership? We perhaps have an unfortunate tendency to rate it in terms of visibility, charisma, clarity, communication, even education and still, rather sadly, class. Surely the only worthwhile measure is in achievement, by the degree to which the leader enables the organisation to realise its intended effects.

References

1. Warren Bennis and Burt Nannis, *Leaders*, Harper and Row 1985

2. T.J. Peters and R.H. Waterman, *In Search of Excellence*, Harper and Row 1982

3. T.J. Peters and N. Austin, *A Passion for Excellence*, Collins 1985.
   (contains an interesting bibliography on the subject)
4. Edgar Schein, *Organisational Culture and Leadership*, Jossey Bass 1985

5. Peter Checkland, *Systems thinking, systems practice*, John Wiley and Sons 1981

6. Henry Mintzberg, *The nature of Managerial Work*, Harper and Row 1973

7. Rosemary Stewart et al, *The District Administrator in the National Health Service*, The King Edward Hospital Fund for London 1980.
8. Rosemary Stewart, *Contrasts in Management*, McGraw Hill 1976

9. J.Kotter and P.R. Lawrence, *Mayors in Action*, Wiley 1974

10. J.Kotter, *The General Manager*, Macmillan 1982

11. J.M. Burns, *Leadership*, Harper and Row 1978

12. BBC Broadcast

13. Warner Burke, (Unpublished Lecture)

Approaching the New Millennium (1993 Edition)

As Clinical Management Teams or Directorates run more and more of the NHS, one of the most important decisions they will make is agreeing who does what . If these teams are to include doctors who continue to practise medicine, then their time is limited and we must keep asking the question " what is it that they and they alone can do?" . The answer for many clinicians will be to provide overall direction in a rapidly changing world and to build a network of powerful supporters, particularly amongst their clinical colleagues - the role of the Transformational Leader. If this is the right choice, then the appointment and development of a cadre of excellent, full-time, Transactional Managers who can work alongside the clinicians is essential. Failure to do so could well destroy the whole clinical management inititiative. Additionally, the heavy focus on management and leadership could encourage people to ignore the much maligned and under-rated process of achieving apparently effortless administration. The accurate calculation of expenditure, the measurement of activity, the ordering of stores, communication with patients, follow up letters to GPs, well organised files - none of these are the stuff of popular management textbooks. "My life running a smooth office" is hardly in the "Troubleshooter" league as a potential best seller. Nevertheless, many trusts are rightly being criticised because of their failure to deliver these simple things and Clinical Directors could easily be dragged away from their unique contribution into putting right activities which do not need their special skills and knowledge.

Summary

All organisations need administrators, managers and leaders. At times of change, it is the transformational leader who provides the vision and cohesion which helps the organisation adjust, without losing its way.

CHANGE AND THE INDIVIDUAL, A CAUSE FOR CONCERN

Chapter 7

There are two tragedies in life. One is not to get your heart's desire. The other is to get it.

George Bernard Shaw

The worst sin towards your fellow creatures is not to hate them but to be indifferent to them: that's the essence of inhumanity.

George Bernard Shaw

We all require stress in order to function. It is the tension of the difference between where we are and where we want to be that energises both people and organisations. Too little stress and we rust away. However, too much and we burn out. Harmful stress can arise from a variety of reasons both at work and at home. In isolation, each factor may be insignificant but the causes of stress seem to be gregarious. They often conspire to mount a mass attack on an individual at one and the same time, at least from the victim's perspective. Often one thing leads to another. Long hours spent coping with overloads at work lead to separation from spouse and family and subsequent marital problems. The uncertainties of mid-career aspirations compete for attention with the demands of wayward adolescent families and neither are given due attention. When individuals are asked to nominate stress raisers, they typically include one-off work events such as:

- Loss of job
- Major change in instructions, policies or procedures
- Major reorganisation
- Change in the nature of work
- Sudden increase in level of activity or pace of work
- New boss
- More hours per week due to crises
- Decrease in status, actual or perceived.

Too much stress - the Effects.

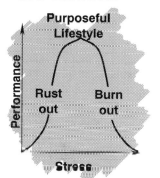

Continuing problems they mention include:

- Too much to do, too little time to do it.
- Conflicting demands from others
- Fire fighting short term problems, which interferes with planned work
- Decisions made which concern them without their involvement
- Attending lengthy meetings
- Conflict between units within the organisation
- Changing priorities
- Lack of confidence in management[1]

Few of the above conditions will be absent when change is around. The current NHS examples are too numerous to list comprehensively. Jobs disappeared when Authorities were abolished, the introduction of general managers has led to the further disappearance of posts, competitive tendering threatens jobs. The shift from institutional to community-based care faces many employees with most of the above issues. New bosses are the norm rather than the exception. They are arriving from different districts, different professions and even a few from outside organisations. Not only are there the usual stresses of accommodating to different personalities, but also the additional ones arising from ex-army officers not behaving like NHS managers and ex-administrators not behaving like nurses. Worse still, a whole range of 'ex-'s are trying to work out how general managers and chief executives behave and, as they mount the necessary learning curve, confusing and, unintentionally, stressing their subordinates.

Who owns the Problem

Many organisations in the private sector have faced similar and perhaps even sharper problems, including collapse of the whole enterprise. An increasing number recognise the issues involved and provide help for the exposed individuals. There are various arguments for so doing, the simplest of which is financial. Even organisations which regard people as "human resources" recognise that they can't afford to have a resource operating at less than 100% efficiency or, worse still, absent and unavailable because of stress-related illness. An organisation like ours, that provides health care, should be at the forefront of such activities but, at the time of writing, this does not appear to be the case. Major reorganisations are clearly having a massive impact on the lives and careers of staff, at all levels. With some notable exceptions, the organisation does not appear to be making a concerted effort to help those most affected.

At another level, overstressed individuals can limit the organisation's change capacity. An individual's reaction to unacceptable levels of change-induced stress may well be to switch off, block the change and be generally unreasonable. Powerful but alienated individuals can drain an organisation's energy and hinder innovation.

However, the most compelling reason for this issue being high on managerial agendas is that, if we really believe that effective people are the foundation for successful enterprises, we must pay attention to the impact of organisational change on them as individuals. The long term impact of the stories that people tell of the way they were treated cannot be over-estimated[2].

Organisational Inertia

If the problem is so obvious and the reasons for taking action so compelling, why the organisational lethargy? Maybe we are collectively overwhelmed, undoubtedly the volume of work involved could appear impossibly large. I suspect that the infinite variety of personalities further compounds the problem. Large, widespread issues seem to require generalised solutions because we haven't the time to deal with them on an individual basis. The variety is however only too real. The level at which acceptable becomes intolerable is very individual and unpredictable; one person's freedom is another's frightening ambiguity. Of two people experiencing similar organisational strains, one will rapidly look for the positives, the other will remain at sea for years on end. We all know the story of one person's half empty glass being another's half full one. A third blockage may well be part of the NHS culture. We no longer have matrons but the syndrome of "when I was a young nurse I scrubbed the floors" is still around and it isn't, and probably never was, confined to nursing. One of the characteristics of those who rise to the top of organisations is almost certainly an above average ability to tolerate ambiguity and change. It is perhaps too easy to say we coped; too difficult to be open about how it felt coping and what it might have cost us. Suppose we can handle the volume and the variety and overcome our cultural prejudices, the next step isn't easy. Who needs help most? Superficially, the competent surgical registrar would be expected to feel more comfortable about her future than the competent domestic, worried by competitive tendering, the spectre of unemployment and effects of it on his family. Limited experience of counselling doctors would refute even this assumption. To quote from Lane Gerber's excellent study of doctors, "When I'm home, I feel guilty because I've been away so much. But if I do try to spend extra time at home, I wonder if I'm getting enough reading done or have done all I could for my patients ... I don't want to ruin my marriage but I don't want to hurt my patients either"[3]. This is one example of a medic. whose interest in general management or management budgeting might, understandably, be less than enthusiastic.

The Context

What can be done? Although this chapter is mainly concerned with the individual's response to change, it is worth briefly considering the context in which the individual is placed. If you work for an enterprise that you believe to be successful, competent and stable, you feel more secure and can tolerate more individual insecurity. The problem is one of perceptions not reality and sometimes perceived security can be counterproductive. The enterprise may, in reality, be on the brink of bankruptcy. However, if the employees "see" the bosses living in the lap of luxury on enormous profits, they won't feel the need to change their working practises because they believe their working environment is secure. In the sixties, the felt, external security of NHS employees was, perhaps, so high that major change programmes were fraught with difficulty. Socialised medicine was the accepted norm. The NHS was at the forefront of innovation in medical care internationally and funds were available for most activities. The unions were a powerful, conservative and protective force. The NHS like many other organisations became complacent. After all, it was the time when "we had never had it so good". Today we might see the NHS as being threatened from all sides, under attack from the private sector, criticised by government, compared unfavourably with other countries and perhaps in danger of losing the affection of its customers. The pendulum has swung from one extreme to the other. Now, the danger is that the overall NHS environment is seen to be so insecure that change will be resisted for opposite reasons. People feel paralysed, unable to cope with change because they work for an organisation that they see as inherently insecure. Before they can help individuals, the first job of today's change managers may well be to build organisational confidence, to provide a more secure environment.

Returning to the individual, what can be done? It often helps to try to get into their shoes, to see things from their point of view, even to remember what it felt like when faced with a similar situation oneself. People often fight change because they foresee an imposition of new ways, a loss of autonomy and self control. General management, speedy decisions, reduced bureaucracy, clear accountability and delegation to the lowest possible level may sound OK to us but how goes it sound to them? At best it might seem uncertain and different. At worst, it could threaten their very existence. If they have developed ways and means for handling things the way they are, they may well be somewhat reluctant to throw them overboard and embrace our brave new world.

When the change affects people very personally, they typically go through four stages, not always in a rational stepwise fashion and certainly at varying speeds. The classic phases are Shock, Defensive Withdrawal, Acknowledgement, Adaptation. Change managers can often achieve their overall aims by being sensitive to these phases and taking appropriate action or sometimes adjusting plans to accommodate them.

Phase 1, Shock

When faced with the shock of change, individuals often feel threatened and overwhelmed. They may experience panic, anxiety and helplessness. Behaviour can become irrational, disorientated and confused. Planning, reasoning and understanding go out of the window - communication channels close down. I remember working with a group of unit staff when the newly appointed DGM was running through his overall plans for the district. He disclosed his intention to reduce the number of units from five to three. I was the only member of the audience to have a clear recollection of the rest of his half-hour presentation; everyone else was fully engaged in processing the fact that they might be out of a job in six months time.

What actions can managers undertake in order to reduce the shock? The best option is to involve the concerned individuals in working out what changes you want to make. The change, when it arrives, will then have been anticipated and, in part, accommodated. This is only credible when there is a real intention of accepting the outcomes of the participation, if they prove, as is likely, to be better than your original intentions. Human being are sophisticated animals with a sixth sense for detecting manipulation and cant. It is not

**Helping
the Individual**

always appropriate to involve people in making the decisions; they may be so threatened by the likely outcomes that this prevents any real debate. It may still be possible to be level with them about your views, to be open about how the problem will be tackled, to keep them informed, even to consult them from time to time. The right decision, when it is finally announced, is then likely to be as obvious to them, as it is to you. When the change is almost certain to be "unacceptable" but nevertheless essential to the organisation, perhaps the best that can be done is to announce the change, recognise the likely effects of the shock and provide for them. For example, there is little room for a participative approach when managing a change which involves the disappearance of a particular task and which will predictably make the participants redundant. Do-it-yourself hangman's kits have never been popular executive toys.

Phase 2, Defensive withdrawal

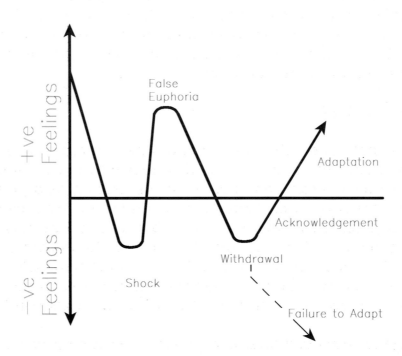

An inability to cope with the shock of the change often leads to a denial of its very existence, a withdrawal into flights of fancy.

People frequently become negative and withdrawn although individuals will sometimes even become euphoric and exhibit false optimism. Nowhere is this more apparent than in the person made redundant, who forgets for the moment that he has a wife, seven children, a mortgage and an overdraft. Instead, he sees the loss of employment as an opportunity to do what he has always dreamt of, even though it will provide no income, which was why he didn't do it in the first place. The manager can perhaps do little to help individuals through this phase. Overtures are likely to be rejected angrily if he pushes the individual to see the world as it really is. The manager's best, in fact perhaps his only option, may be to press on in various ways, keeping the issue on the table, hoping that in so doing the individual will come to recognise that it won't just go away.

Phase 3, Acknowledgement

The time usually arrives when the change can no longer be ignored and the new reality is recognised. This phase if often akin to a period of bereavement. People continue to look backwards to practises which in retrospect seem attractive. It is a time of little directed energy, the individual may well become apathetic. "If that's the way it's going to be, let them get on with it". Usually when people have got this far, which may take five minutes or five years, the manager's task is relatively simple and centres around providing ways in which the individual can contribute positively to the new situation and move towards the final phase.

Phase 4, Adaptation

In this final phase, the individual begins to mobilise his or her personal resources and abilities to meet the new situation. Managers can help most by recognising it as a period of personal growth, providing opportunities for involvement, challenge, job enrichment, on the job coaching, training and development. This is the fun bit if the individual gets that far, which tragically isn't inevitable. How many people do we all know who switched off somewhere in the first three phases and are now trying to sit it out until retirement?

Change for the individual is basically a learning process. It often begins with feelings of dis-equilibrium, incompetence and discomfort. This dissonance leads to a drive to restore equilibrium. Possible negative consequences are that individuals reject, suppress and distort their perceptions of reality rather than face the inevitable stress of handling it. The effective change manager will, however, find ways to help and encourage them towards the positive outcomes of exploring alternatives, developing new behaviours, of adaptation, accommodation and individual growth.

Whole Life Transitions

Without attempting to discuss the problem in depth, these transitions at work have a nasty habit of coinciding with the wider, whole person transitions, which seem to be a feature of most of our lives. It is worth recognising that some of us have enough trouble working through our life transitions, without having to cope with extra obstacles thrown in from changes at work. For career men, the life transitions seem to happen around the ages of 30, 40, 53 and with approaching retirement. The 40 year one often proves the most turbulent, although it may not justify the popular phrase of mid-life crisis. There are probably too few British career women to make any definitive statements but, for a woman's view, interested managers would do well to read Gail Sheehy's book on the subject[4].

Organisation-wide Responses- Counselling & Self-development

Are there any organisation-wide activities which will help? It is worth considering two, counselling and self-development. Both help individuals strengthen their internal security and hence increase their capacity to handle uncertainty and change. Both are known to be effective in practise[5,6.] Both are congruent with the future if you believe the future will see an increase in self-help, autonomy and participation.

The word counselling is used here in a special and perhaps confusing sense, a sense which in many ways is the antithesis of the dictionary definition - advising, recommending, urging adoption. In this context, counselling is seen as a process in which individuals are helped to help themselves, a non-directive and certainly non-judgemental, confidential process in which people are able to come to terms with their feelings, identify their options, choose between them and marshal their own inner resources, in order to overcome the problems they face. This definition is that of an expert professional counsellor[5]. The match between the solution and the change problems described above is immediately obvious. Who should counsel? Caring managers may well wish to. Effective managers use counselling skills, particularly when they coach. There are, however, inherent problems in managers counselling their subordinates. Is it possible to establish a relationship which one day is non-directive and "client-centred" and on the next day to return to being judgemental? Secondly, counselling is a whole person activity, which touches on areas not normally talked about between boss and subordinate and which, if explored, can raise ethical problems. What does the manager do if, in counselling sessions, he is told of issues which as a manager he judges could damage the organisation? Will a counselled subordi-

subordinate disclose to his boss issues which might reduce his promotion prospects? If, as is often the case, the boss looms large as a problem in the eyes of the subordinate, how will this be handled? There are opposite points of view[7] and there will be exceptions, but, as a rule, managers do not help if they try to adopt a counselling role. Better alternatives are to employ specially trained counsellors, internally or externally, or to establish a climate where peer counselling is acceptable or perhaps a combination of all of these with a listening management style.

Independent Counselling	Managerial Advice
Situationally Ignorant	Situationally Expert
Structured Listening	Give Information
Non—Directive	Tend to Control
Confront Emotions	Avoid Embarrassment
Empathise	Sympathise
Whole Person Approach	Concentrate on Work

Self-awareness raising and self-development activities are complementary. Studies of effective managers[8] reveal that they usually have a realistic appreciation of their own capabilities. They know what they can do and act accordingly. Increasingly, organisations are recognising the value of mounting activities which allow individuals "space" to reflect on their personal preferences, skills, capabilities, habits, values, short and long term goals and which lead to self development programmes, implemented and agreed with their "bosses". The general philosophy is one of helping individuals improve their capacity to respond to the demands that a changing and uncertain future presents and to take charge of their own careers. There is a growing body of anecdotal evidence that this approach is valued within the service, as well as outside it.

References:

1. John Adams, *Coping with Stress at Work*, edited by Marshall and Cooper, Gower   Press 1981

2. Deal and Kennedy, *Corporate Cultures, the rites and rituals of corporate life*, Adison-Wesley 1982

3. Lane Gerber, *Married to their careers,* Tavistock 1983

4. Gail Sheehy, *Passages,* Clarke and Irwin 1974

5. A. Milne, *Counselling in Industry,* Personnel Executive, January, March 1982

6. T. Pedlar, J. Burgoyne and T. Boydell, *A Managers Guide to Self Development,* McGraw Hill 1978

7. Peters and Austin, *A Passion for Excellence,* Collins 1985

8. J. Kotter, *The General Managers,* McMillan 1982: J. Kotter and P. Lawrence, *Mayors in Action,* Wiley 1974

9. A. Milne, *Private communication*

Approaching the New Millennium (1993 Edition)

In the 80s, the message was clear. Where are all the trainees to be found to staff the Service? In particular, how do we recruit and retain nurses? Yet, in the last few years, we have seen nurses and midwives complete their training but fail to find employment. The shake up following the Tomlinson Report is leading to redeployment and resettlement on a scale few would have envisaged ten years ago. For many of us, security and job tenure have disappeared. For some who see life as a learning opportunity, the upheavals have presented them with exciting new challenges - physiotherapists have become business managers, doctors general managers, nurses chief executives. Some who have taken charge of their careers have been amply rewarded. Sadly, society at large continues to struggle to adjust to new technologies which require fewer staff and has yet to find ways of dealing with those whose work disappears as a result of organisations succeeding in "doing more with less". Many have found their career expectations truncated through no fault of their own. The stresses described above remain - even the best organisations still struggle to help their staff adjust.

Summary

Change is often a period of major stress for the individuals involved. If they wish to manage efficient and successful enterprises, managers need to help staff handle these stresses. There is no one predictable reaction to change but there are common patterns which managers can anticipate and helpful steps that they can take to improve the individual's capacity to respond to change in a positive way. Two activities, which are congruent with probable future paradigms, are to provide counselling support and encourage individual self-awareness/development programmes.

PART 2
CHANGE TOOLS AND TECHNIQUES

This part of the book provides a kit of well proven tools which organisations can use to work through some of their key change issues. They cover the most common ones and are placed in a reasonably rational order.

Individuals may well use them to clarify their own ideas but they are most effective when used by groups, as part of a planned change process, particularly when a neutral third party, familiar with them, can act as a consultant to the groups.

APPENDIX 1
CHECKING THE ORGANISATION'S HEALTH

The following form lists 22 characteristics of an organisation. Firstly, on the scale of 1 to 8, rate your organisation, as it is today, by putting crosses in the appropriate boxes. (N.B. "never true" to the left, "always true" to the right).

Having completed the list, repeat the exercise, this time putting a tick in the box that, in your view, represents the ideal organisation.

The difference between the tick and the cross, provides an indication of how far you see your organisation from being healthy. The individual differences can be averaged to produce an overall rating. Where individuals place the marks on each scale will be very subjective but the value of the differences can be compared in a group. In this way it is possible to check the diagnosis of the need for change.

Are there some immediate actions that could be taken to improve things? Are there any improvements which are especially important for the particular change programme being worked on?

	Never true						Always true	
	1	2	3	4	5	6	7	Diff
1. Consistent high quality service is emphasised at all times.								
2. The organisation responds to the needs and views of the patients.								
3. The organisation is well in touch with its environment - has its finger on the pulse of things.								
4. The public sees the organisation as friendly.								
5. The organisation's leaders create an exciting working environment.								
6. Managers are visible and well known - they regularly "walk the floor."								
7. Staff know what their leaders stand for.								
8. The organisation has a well defined and explicit set of beliefs.								
9. General objectives are set and widely shared.								

	Never true						Always true	
	1	2	3	4	5	6	7	Diff
10. Information is widely shared - managers are open with their staff.								
11. Conflict is managed not suppressed.								
12. The organisation will try out new ideas and experiment without lengthy debate - analysis does not lead to paralysis.								
13. People are encouraged to be entrepreneurial, creative and innovative.								
14. Failure is seen as an opportunity to learn and a natural part of life.								
15. Managers assume that individuals want to take on more responsibility and provide opportunities for them to do so.								
16. An effort is made to inspire people throughout the organisation.								
17. Managers demonstrate respect for people and treat them as adults.								
18. People work effectively together in multi-disciplinary teams.								
19. People are more concerned with contributing to overall success than defending their own professional or personal affairs.								
20. Casual, unstructured, seemingly random yet task-related meetings frequently happen.								
21. The organisation's form is simple and easily understood.								
22. The organisation is well disciplined and tightly organised towards its key tasks yet allows flexibility and provides headroom for its staff.								

How would you rate your organisation in terms of its overal effectiveness?

One of the best	*Better than many*	*OK, generally gets the job done*	*Effective in some areas*	*Marginally effective*
☐	☐	☐	☐	☐

APPENDIX 2
AGREEING THE CORE PURPOSE

Defining the core purpose of the enterprise is an attempt to answer the question "as a purposeful human activity system, what is it that we uniquely do?" or "what is it that distinguishes our contribution to some larger system?".

Core purposes (sometimes called missions) are not objectives. Objectives can be reached and new ones set. Core purposes define the basic reason for the organisation's existence and persist. They may be adjusted over time but when they disappear, the organisation as we knew it goes with them.

The core purpose of an organisation exists in our individual minds. Because of our different values we may wish to see the organisation have different purposes. Because of the imperfections of human communication, we may believe we share the same view of the core purpose but in reality are poles apart. We may never have thought about it deeply, just assumed that everyone knows what we are about. It is however vital to be crystal clear about an organisation's core purpose, as it is the final reference point which binds the organisation together and steers it through the chaos of change.

The core purpose of a prison might be seen as:

- To keep criminals away from society

- To punish criminals

- To rehabilitate offenders

- To deter citizens from criminal activities

- A university of crime, to teach criminality to the inmates

It may be more than one of these, it may, in part, be all of them but agreement on which is the core purpose, the one that has precedence, will determine how we shape our prisons in future.

Write a sentence describing the core purpose of your organisation in terms of what it does. Good definitions will include a simple statement of the central transformation that the organisation carries out on behalf of specified "owners". They will often contain potentially conflicting statements, e.g. "to make a profit whilst providing continuing work for our employees". It can be helpful to include clauses about whoever is on the receiving end of your activities, the ones who benefit from or suffer as a result of what you do, the clients. The people who carry out the activity usually feature. If, as is likely, the group cannot immediately agree, again ask the question "who owns the system?". What is the owner's view of the core purpose? Put in a clause about them.

It is not unusual for groups to fail to agree on the fine print, first time. At worst, settle for written statements of different core purposes and agree to come back to them. Plan ways of resolving the differences later.

An example of a core purpose for a particular nursing home was judged to be:

"To provide homely, community-based accommodation for severely physically disabled elderly people so that they achieve the best possible quality of life, with substantial freedom for individual choice, whilst providing necessary nursing care, security and safety and operating within the available resources."

APPENDIX 3
MAPPING THE ENVIRONMENT

Think of your bit of the organisation as being at the centre of its universe, surrounded by individual key people, groups, other systems, regulations, abstract ideas, all of which could be important to the success of your change programme. Put these domains on a flipchart, like the spokes of a wheel. This particular format allows additional domains to be slotted in, at appropriate points on the circle, as they come to mind. The aim is to produce something like this.

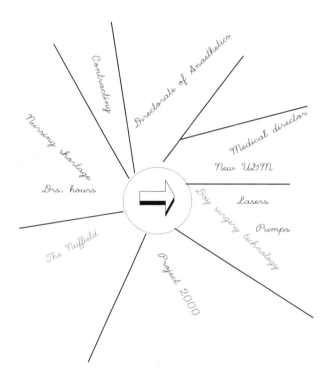

The domains are likely to include groups of influential people, people in authority, government bodies, pressure groups, other authorities, representatives, media, consumers, suppliers, institutions, professions, bosses, other bits of your organisation, cooperating or competing organisations, technologies, laws, policies, procedures, information, and so on.

There is no way that all these domains can be handled. Reduce the comprehensive chart to half a dozen or so that seem particularly vital. It may be possible to combine some. One good test of the need for attention is to ask "Can I plan to neglect this domain? Will anything go wrong if I do?"

Having selected the key domains, ask the question "what demands does this domain make of us now and how do we respond". Your GPs might demand prompt letters about patients seen by your organisation; the current response of your bit of the organisation may be to agree but fail to deliver. Are the current demands and responses satisfactory or do they need changing?

Listing the current demands and responses of the key domains is one part of building a picture of the organisation's current state.

APPENDIX 4
PAINTING A VISION OF THE FUTURE

Without wanting to enter the realms of idle dreaming, it can be important to find ways of getting feet, if not totally in the clouds, at least out of the clinging concrete of today's problems. A clear, shared vision of a desired future state, is a proven tool for encouraging and shaping change.

A stimulating method is to look ahead, three, five or ten years as you judge appropriate. Paint a picture in words, drawings or both, of what you would hope to see your organisation doing. If you could climb into a helicopter and look down and take a photograph or shoot a video to show your children, what would people be up to? If you were writing a storyboard for your ideal television documentary of the enterprise, what scenes would you include, what would the shooting script be like? Think operationally, who would be doing what, when and where with whom? Cover hard data, facts and tasks but also include the human things - individual behaviour, feelings, emotions and values. Consider the management, the rest of the employees, the clients and the key domains of your environment. Will they still be key? If so what demands will they make then? What would you like them to make?

Mind mapping ™ (cf. Appendix 8, The Work to be done) can be used to a record a picture temporarily but it is worth actually writing a scenario of the future state and taking a couple of pages to do it.

Questions which can sharpen the vision of the future would include:

(i)   What are the major trends in the way our society is moving? What is the significance of them for us?

(ii) What would our most important stakeholders want us to look like in "X" years time? How will they measure our performance?

(iii) What would happen if we continue down our present path, without making any significant shift?

(iv) Where would early warning signals come from that would cause us to change our direction? Are there any transmitting alarms now?

(v)   What are the critical external events which could happen in the next "X" years? How probable are they? What can we do internally and in managing our environment to make the most of the opportunities they present and to minimise the effect of any threats?

Example

A group spent some time developing a future scenario describing part of their vision for care of the elderly:

"Looking at the detail in one imaginary District, the core group is chaired by the Medical Director, a consultant physician who until a couple of years ago had little interest in this field but took on the task at the request of the General Manager. Today there is an element of celebration as the group are hosting a buffet lunch to mark the formal opening of the 'St Michael's Centre'. This is a new experimental unit built jointly by the LA and the NHS, in the grounds of the old Maternity Hospital using part of the existing buildings. It provides some short stay care wards for the elderly ill, a Day Hospital and a Day Centre, as well as the residential home for those who need nursing care. The unit has in fact been operational for some time and as well as providing a service of its own, it is used as a teaching unit for workers in this field from the NHS and the LA. The unit was funded partially from the NHS, partially from the LA and partially from voluntary sources. The community as a whole was involved in its establishment, the fund raising and community liaison aspects of the project being managed by a senior manager from a national chain store, who was seconded to the project as part of an action learning programme.

Before lunch, the core group held their regular monthly meeting. One of the main items on the agenda was a review of the pilot scheme for the posts of home care assistants. These jobs have been created to provide, in one individual, skills in domestic assistance, simple nursing care and elements of occupational/physiotherapy. The job grading still remains something of a problem as it crosses the boundaries of the old NHS job assessment scheme and the LA scheme. Operationally the system is working well. In the pilot locality, trained nursing staff have been released to man a 24 hour service of more intensive nursing care for those elderly discharged from hospital and to work with the Geriatrician and GPs on care of the terminally ill. The core group resolved to accept the pilot group's report and recommend to the management board that ..." etc.

APPENDIX 5
SHARING PRIORITIES

Priorities always have to be set and choices made. Decisions can of course be imposed but it is often useful to explore the preferences of key individuals and to understand what lies behind their aspirations, for the following reasons:

(i) Major change is based on their commitment and motivation.

(ii) Judgements in our service are often subjective, exploring what lies behind their judgements will lead to better decisions.

(iii) It builds consensus. There is often more agreement than is apparent, we disagree about our first preference but share the same top half dozen. If there is a major conflict about priorities, it is better to have it out in the open than simmering beneath the surface, draining the energy of the group.

Ranking Techniques

To use this method, first list the issues that you wish to compare on a grid; each individual using the same list but for the first part of the exercise working independently and privately:

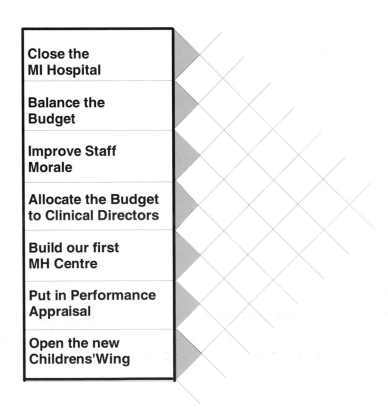

Next, still working independently, compare the pairs of issues, one with another. In the example, decide whether, if you can't do both, you would "close the MI Hospital" or "balance the budget". If it is the upper one of the pair put a tick in the diamond where the lines intersect; if it is the lower put a cross.

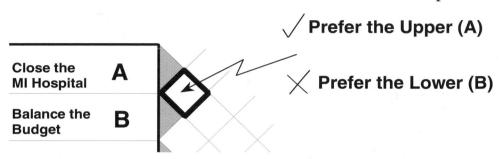

Now, similarly, compare "closing the MI hospital" with "improving morale".

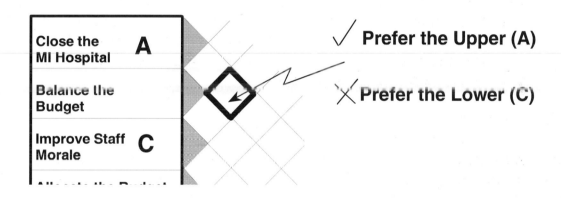

In this way, every possible comparison can be made.

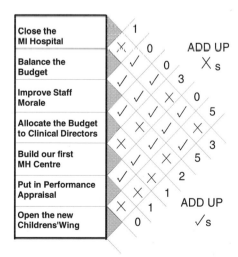

Next, total the diagonal columns; in the rising ones adding crosses, in the falling one ticks. For example, in the illustration the rising diagonal which starts at "building our first MH Home" has three crosses and scores 3, the falling one has one tick and scores 1. Add these together giving a total of 4 for "building our first MH Centre".

Repeating this process and arranging the activities in order would give:

Balance the Budget	6 points
Open the children's wing	5 points
Build our first MH centre	4 points
Close the MI Hospital	3 points
Improve staff morale	2 points
Introduce budgets for doctors	1 point
Put in performance appraisal	0 points

Assuming this is a group activity, share the results, putting scores onto a flip chart, showing not the points but the ranked positions, thus:

Recognise the measure of agreement and also explore where there is conflict.

	Jack	Joe	Jim	Jill	Jean	Avge
Close MI Hospital	3	2	3	3	2	2.6
Balance the Budget	6	6	6	5	6	5.8
Improve Morale	2	5	0	1	4	2.4
Allocate Budget	1	1	2	2	1	1.4
Build MI Centre	4	3	4	4	3	3.6
Performance Appraisal	0	0	1	0	0	0.2
Children's Wing	5	4	5	6	5	5.0

In the illustration, there was unanimity on most things, as is often the case, but on one issue there was conflict. Two participants ranked "improving staff morale" high, everyone else ranked it low. The two dissidents saw morale as the key to everything else and they sensed that people were so dispirited that, unless this could be improved, nothing else would be achieved. The example, which is drawn from life, confirmed the need to control expenditure and com-mission the new wing but also persuaded the group to gather more information about the state of the troops, in order to see who was right.

APPENDIX 6
FORCE FIELD ANALYSIS

This tool is useful when you know where you want to go but are stuck or making unacceptably slow progress. The analysis enables you to work out the forces driving and opposing the desired change and to take actions which are likely to produce movement. It can be used by individuals but is particularly effective when used in a group of two to six people, who want to open up their thinking. The model is like the surgeon's knife, by itself it is completely neutral, how you wield it is up to you. It can be used to manipulate your opponents, equally it can elevate a group's mutual understanding of the mess they are in and lead to solutions which benefit everyone.

(i) The technique first requires a description of the situation at the start of your change programme and a shared vision of a desired future state. If these do not exist, scribble them down on a flip chart so that they are at the forefront of everyone's mind and can trigger thoughts.

(ii) Draw up a list of forces which are pushing in the direction of the change and a list of those opposing it.

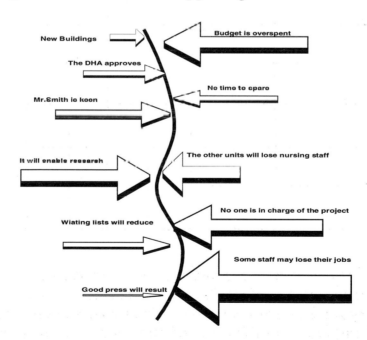

Write them up on a flipchart using arrows to indicate their direction and relative strengths. Concentrate on the forces, perceived or real, as they apply to the group experiencing the situation not to those doing the analysis. Rationalists will find it useful to work through the following force types in sequence:

Personal
Inter-personal
Inter-group
Managerial
Organisational
Technological
Environmental

Less logical thinkers might favour brainstorming, then eliminating the irrelevant and finally using the above as a check list.

(iii) Look at the restraining forces and see what can be done to reduce them or redirect them elsewhere. The temptation is always to push harder - brick walls seem to induce headbanging. However, if the restraining forces are reduced, the change will move quietly forward, just as surely but with less danger of generating new opposing forces. There is no justification for extrapolating Newtonian physics into the realms of human behaviour but experience shows that actions generate opposing reactions here, just as in the world of mechanics. For example, increasing the pressure on people to retire early may generate strong union opposition, which did not exist before, in order to protect jobs. Action produces a reaction.

It may even be that, inadvertently, some of the restraining forces owe their existence to pressures you have already generated and that, somewhat paradoxically, a reduction of a pushing force will be helpful.

(iv) Is there action that needs to be taken to maintain the pushing forces? Are there some pushing forces that can be introduced or increased without significantly increasing resistance?

(v) Have you all the data you need? Do you need to check out some of your assumptions?

(vi) Next assess whether there is a realistic chance of getting anywhere. It may be that, now that the problem is clearer, it is clearly impossible. Is it sensible to settle for a less desirable but achievable future? Would the available energy be better used on other change programmes?

(vii) If the decision is made to continue and a number of desirable actions have been identified, all that remains is to decide who is going to do what, by when etc.

REMINDER: Reduce the restraining forces.
Beware reaction from increasing the pushing forces.
Write an action plan.

Example

Closure of a small cottage hospital and transfer of patients and staff to the new DGH

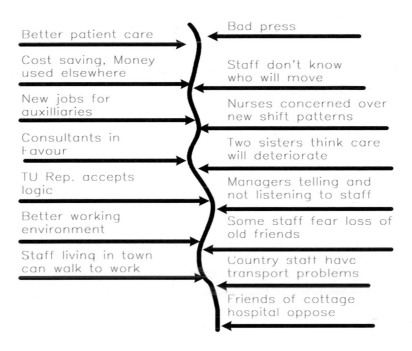

Better patient care	Bad press
Cost saving, Money used elsewhere	Staff don't know who will move
New jobs for auxilliaries	Nurses concerned over new shift patterns
Consultants in favour	Two sisters think care will deteriorate
TU Rep. accepts logic	Managers telling and not listening to staff
Better working environment	Some staff fear loss of old friends
Staff living in town can walk to work	Country staff have transport problems
	Friends of cottage hospital oppose

Actions

(a) Invite the editor of the local paper to visit both facilities.

(b) Run a "training workshop" for all first line managers, spell out the need for them to talk over the problems of moving with each member of their staff. Provide pack of information for these managers. Include skills training on positive listening and later collect feedback from them in order to plan general response.

(c) Provide access to a more expert neutral counsellor, once a week, so that individuals can work through their individual problems arising from the move.

(d) Clinical nurse manager to work with the two reluctant sisters to identify their concerns and plan to resolve them.

(e) Establish a small working party (Clinical Nurse Manager, Ward Sister, Staff Nurse) to examine options for nursing shift systems and report back, in first instance to Clinical Director.

(f) Use managers to identify transport problems of any individuals, spell out policy on temporary payments & etc.

APPENDIX 7
THE CHANGE EQUATION
(Developed by David Gleicher)

When you feel the need to understand why a key individual doesn't buy your favourite scheme and you are looking for ways to get him or her on board, the change equation is a powerful tool. Despite its name it isn't mathematical, even though we will begin in the time honoured algebraic style.

Let A = the individual's level of dissatisfaction with things the way they are now

Let B = the individual's vision of a better future

Let C = an acceptable first step

and D = the cost to the individual of making the change

Individuals will resist change unless:

$$A + B + C > D$$

Some people sharpen the tool by stating a corollary thus:

For change to occur, $A \times B \times C > 0$

The basis of the pseudo-mathematics is that making a change always costs an individual something, represented by "D". It may be money, resources, it often is time and can be psychological trivia or trauma.

Individuals therefore tend to resist change. For the resistance to be overcome, the individual must believe that the cost is worthwhile. (A + B + C) must in total be sufficiently large to overcome the cost (D).

"A", Felt dissatisfaction with the way things are.

If the current situation is felt to be comfortable, change will be difficult - the fat cat syndrome. People may also have come to tolerate a poor situation from force of habit. If they don't feel any pain they won't have much incentive to work on making things better. We commonly assume that our dissatisfaction is shared by others, when this may not be the case.

"B", A shared vision of a better future.

If there is no clarity of vision about the probable outcome of the change or, even worse, the vision is clear but seen as a retrograde step, commitment to the change is going to be hard to buy. For change to be sustained, the vision needs to be shared by the group who are involved and agreed by them. If individuals disagree about where they are going the likelihood is that they will fall out on the journey.

"C", First practical steps.

Even when "A" and "B" are sufficiently large, change often fails because the first step isn't obvious or looks impossibly large. A "yesable proposition" describes what is necessary, even if it is Americanese. First steps are most acceptable when they involve pushing small pebbles down from the top of the hill, rather than boulders up from the bottom.

The corollary, A x B x C > 0, suggests that if any of "A, B or C" are zero, nothing will happen.

The tool can be used to identify whether individuals will join the change effort and often to identify work that has to be done to gain their commitment. It can equally be used to examine groups or systems and the same principles will apply.

Example

A consultant physician runs an out-patient clinic where it is commonplace for patients to suffer two hour delays before seeing him. There is a management-led campaign to improve the image of the hospital in the eyes of its customers and the consultant is a key figure as the clinic staff look to him for leadership. He shows little interest in the campaign.

The analysis produced the following conclusions.

"A". The consultant was known to be dissatisfied with the way his clinic worked. He felt overloaded and unable to give a reasonable amount of attention to each patient. However, because of the overload, he became very frustrated if there were any gaps between appointments. His answer was to make block bookings. He knew patients sometimes complained to the administration but generally he felt that they had come to tolerate the delays as being typical of the NHS. The administrative or nursing staff usually calmed any angry patients down, reasonable well, before he met them.

"B". He believed the hospital was underfunded and that he was overworked because of shortage of clinical staff. Some problems he attributed to a shortage of radiographers. He also believed ambulances were not available to bring patients to the clinic in a planned fashion. In his view, there was no prospect of money being available to put these things right. He had no vision of things getting better.

"C". His clinic was one of many; he therefore felt that the problem needed to be worked on jointly with his colleagues. The last time it had been raised at the Medical Staff Committee, the debate had degenerated into a monologue from "Fred" about "privatisation" and he couldn't see any way that his colleagues would agree to look at the problem in a rational manner.

The action decided upon was to provide administrative assistance to look at the reasons for the gaps in the consultant's schedule, with the aim of producing a more rational workload for him by ironing out the peaks and troughs - a simple first step, the "yesable proposition", worthwhile in its own right and likely to lead naturally in the overall direction of the campaign. The object of the change programme moved temporarily from introducing consumerism to motivating a key person (cf. commitment planning).

APPENDIX 8
THE WORK TO BE DONE

The volume of work generated by change programmes can be so large and varied that it becomes difficult to keep track of what is going on. A number of
techniques are useful.

Clustering

Write down individual tasks, as they are identified, on cards, or better still
Post-Its (those sticky bits of coloured paper that generate millions of pounds of
business for 3M each year). The individual items can then be grouped and
regrouped in different clusters. The human brain can handle ten clusters better
than 201 different, individual items. If you are so inclined and the list is large
enough, computers can do the same sort of thing, almost as quickly. The clus-
tering can be based on previous experience, looking for work associated with
predetermined "headings", e.g. training, structures, customers, clinicians etc.
or the data itself can be used to generate the group titles. The Post-It method
works well in groups.

Mind Mapping

Tony Buzan (Use Your Head, BBC Publications) suggested a technique which
enables the whole picture to be seen at a glance.

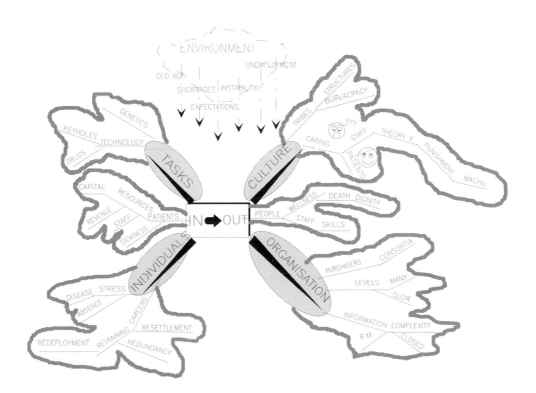

Each issue is represented by a key word, which will later trigger the writers' memory. The key words are then underlined and linked to form a network. The use of colour and pictures makes the charts more easily understood. It is also worth using block letters; firstly, because they are more readily taken in and, secondly, because it can be very frustrating if the key words cannot be deciphered later! The Buzan Mind Map™ is particularly valued by those of us who don't think sequentially and therefore find normal lists frustrating.

The Domino Effect

Most people have played the children's game of lining up dominoes in patterns. When the appropriate domino is pushed, all the rest fall down. The same may be true of the change tasks. Is there a key domino?

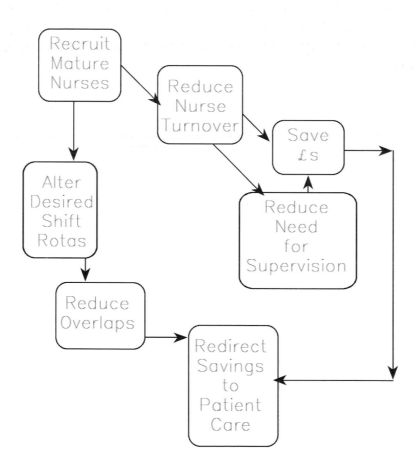

A Hierarchy of Objectives

It is often possible to classify emerging issues as aspirations, strategic objectives, tactical goals and first steps.

Aspirations are long term, open ended statements which tend to be "for motherhood and against sin". They generate little energy or conflict, e.g. we would all concur with "We need to provide better standards of care for the elderly".

Strategic objectives are realistic statements of what has to be done by a particular time but in the longer term. They represent those activities which shape the way the organisation aims to respond to changes in the environment. They generate argument at the level of values. "In five years time, over 99% of the District's budget for the elderly will be allocated to caring for those elderly who are significantly physically and/or mentally disabled".

Tactical goals are half-way stages which provide the energy that drives the change. They can become the responsibility of specific individuals or groups, who are held publicly accountable for achieving them, given appropriate resources. "In 1987, we will open a residential home for 30 severely physically-disabled elderly people. The home will provide homely facilities and operate in a way which respects the individual freedom of its residents".

First Steps are those things which can be done immediately to make action legitimate and often signal the intention to move towards the strategic goal. "Organise a survey of property in the locality which could be converted into a home for the elderly".

APPENDIX 9
COMMITMENT PLANNING

In every organisation there are key people and groups who exert power and who can help or hinder your change programme. They may be in positions of authority, the district general manager, the chairman of the health authority. They may be long serving staff whose influence extends far beyond their position in the organisation, whose opinions are trusted by more powerful people. They can be people respected by their colleagues because of their professional competence. They can be people who are very mobile - the information specialist. They may control key or scarce resources. Some will be outside the organisation and already identified during environmental mapping. Some will be built into the critical mass which will fuel the change programme. Others need consideration because they can block progress.

Gaining the commitment of this key group is work and therefore justifies a certain amount of planning. Two charting systems can help identify that work.

Commitment Planning

Write the key people down one side of a sheet of paper and across the top put the following headings to indicate their level of commitment:

No commitment; likely to oppose the change

Let; will not oppose the change but will not positively assist you

Help; will support the change if someone else leads

Make: will lead the change process, want to make it happen

Against each individual, put an O to indicate where they are at present and an X to indicate where they need to be if you are to succeed. The difference between the two indicates the workload. It may be that you have to curb some inappropriate enthusiasm as well as generate commitment.

	Oppose	*Let*	*Support*	*Make*
General Manager			X ◄——— O	
Chairman	O ——►X			
Director of operations		X O		
Director of finance		O ——►X		
Project manager				XO
Personnel officer		X ◄——— O		

Readiness and Capability Charting

This slightly different approach is particularly helpful in thinking about the readiness and capability of the critical mass. Readiness is about their motivation, their enthusiasm for the change. Capability is a measure of their ability to deliver or, to use a northern expression, their clout. They may be very enthusiastic but can't persuade their boss, or they don't have the contacts, or are short of information; all issues where their "capability" can be helped. List the key actors you have chosen to make up your critical mass, rate their readiness and capability as high, medium or low. Focus on the work to be done to make up deficiencies.

KEY ACTORS	Readiness			Capability		
	H	M	L	H	M	L
Joanne	✔			✔		
Sir John		✔		✔		
Jack	✔					✔
...er			✔	✔		
			✔		✔	
						✔

APPENDIX 10
ALLOCATING RESPONSIBILITY

This is a simple mechanism for clarifying who is responsible for what, which has the additional advantage of registering agreement to commitment. It is most effective when used in a group, writing the outcomes of a flip chart for all to see, after debating and reaching agreement on the statements. It has also been used to agree the continuing roles of team members.

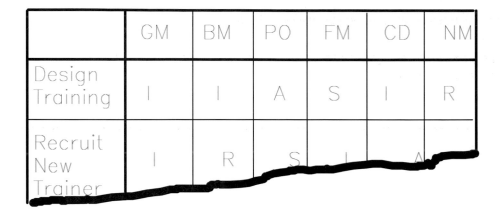

	GM	BM	PO	FM	CD	NM
Design Training	I	I	A	S	I	R
Recruit New Trainer	I	R	S	I		A

List the necessary activities down one side of the paper and the people who are involved across the top.

Take each activity in turn and first decide who is going to be responsible for making it happen. Decide who will drive away from the meeting and feel "that one is down to me". If it is difficult to reach agreement, try breaking the activity down into several parts. An alternative is to ask someone more senior to allocate the responsibility for you.

Put R = Responsible in the appropriate box

RULE 1: Never have two Rs against any activity

Now decide who has to approve, i.e. has the right to veto the decision and must therefore be informed before action is implemented.

Put A = Approve in the appropriate box.

RULE 2: Minimise the As, too many produce delays

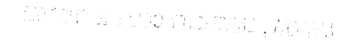

Agree who is going to support the action, i.e. provide resources to help but will not veto what is done.

Put S = Support in the appropriate box

RULE 3: Agree what support means in real terms

Settle who will just be kept informed, without any right to veto and can therefore, if necessary, be informed after the event.

Put I = Informed in the appropriate box

RULE 4:   If you mean approve rather than inform don't be mealy mouthed (but see rule 2)